ELEMENTARY
Vocabulary Practice Book

in
English

PETER VINEY
KAREN VINEY

OXFORD
UNIVERSITY PRESS

Contents

Word games 3

Key: Word games 16

Picture dictionary 19

Key: Picture dictionary 44

Everyday English 51

Test yourself 75

Reading for pleasure 83

Word games

Word Games

Numbers

Look at these film titles. Underline the numbers (1, 2, 3 …).
Circle the ordinal numbers (1st, 2nd …).

1. The Ten Commandments
2. Twelfth Night
3. Forty-Second Street
4. Forty-Eight Hours
5. The Forty-Ninth Parallel
6. First Knight
7. The Seventh Voyage of Sinbad
8. The Three Worlds of Gulliver
9. The Two-Thousand-Year-Old Man
10. Five Days One Summer

Languages

Circle the country with a different language, e.g.

Spain	Mexico	(Brazil)	Argentina
Australia	Canada	Italy	Ireland
Portugal	Mozambique	Colombia	Brazil
France	Belgium	Scotland	Switzerland
Greece	Germany	Austria	Switzerland
Egypt	Saudi Arabia	Morocco	China
The USA	The UK	Turkey	South Africa

Odd one out

Circle the different word in each line.

purple	cold	orange	pink
jeans	shirt	trousers	shorts
mini-bar	bedroom	bathroom	living room
shoes	boots	shorts	trainers
butter	milk	fish	cheese

Food (1)

Find the food words, e.g. LEPAP *apple*

RUBETT	GRASU	LAST	EERPPP	SEAP
TOTOAM	TATOOP	GRANEO	RBWASYERRT	COPPORN
SHANCO	EACK	CHOOTLACE	NODTU	ASTOT

Songs

Underline the main verbs in these song titles.

	SONG	ARTIST
01	Don't <u>Stop</u>	Fleetwood Mac
02	Don't <u>Worry</u>, <u>Be</u> Happy	Bobby McFerrin
03	Don't <u>Go</u> Near The Water	The Beach Boys
04	<u>Be</u> My Baby	The Ronettes
05	Don't <u>Be</u> Cruel	Elvis Presley
06	Don't <u>Think</u> Twice, It's Alright	Bob Dylan
07	Don't <u>Cry</u> For Me, Argentina	Julie Covington
08	Don't <u>Look</u> Now	Bryan Adams
09	Don't <u>Be</u> Angry	Bad Manners
10	Baby Please Don't <u>Go</u>	Them (with Van Morrison)

Money

Add words to the word map.

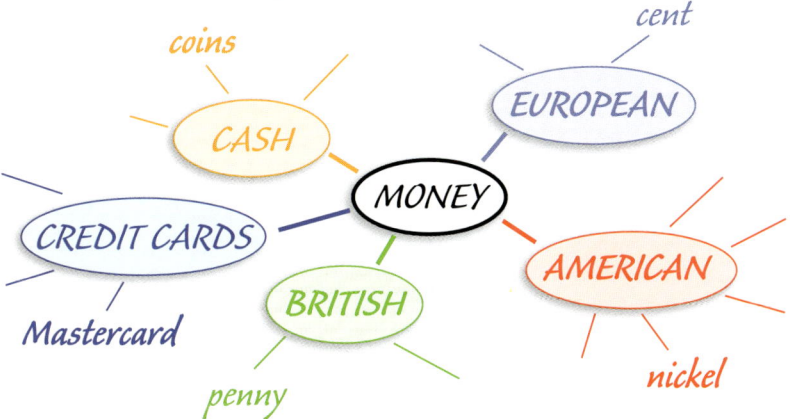

Male or female?

Look at these film titles. Have they got a male or a female word in them? Underline the male words and circle the female words.

1 Charley's (Aunt)
2 <u>Lord</u> Of The Rings
3 The (Lady) And The <u>Tramp</u>
4 <u>Batman</u> Forever
5 O <u>Brother</u>, Where Art Thou?
6 (Mrs) Doubtfire
7 <u>Prince</u> Of Egypt
8 The <u>General's</u> (Daughter)
9 The <u>Man</u> Who Wasn't There
10 The (Princess) Bride

Food (2)
Circle the different word in each line.

pasta	salad	pizza	spaghetti
chicken	lemon	burger	ham
strawberry	apple	melon	cheese
potato	salt	pepper	sugar
fries	chips	potato	cake
donut	pea	potato	tomato

Food (3)
Add words to the word map.

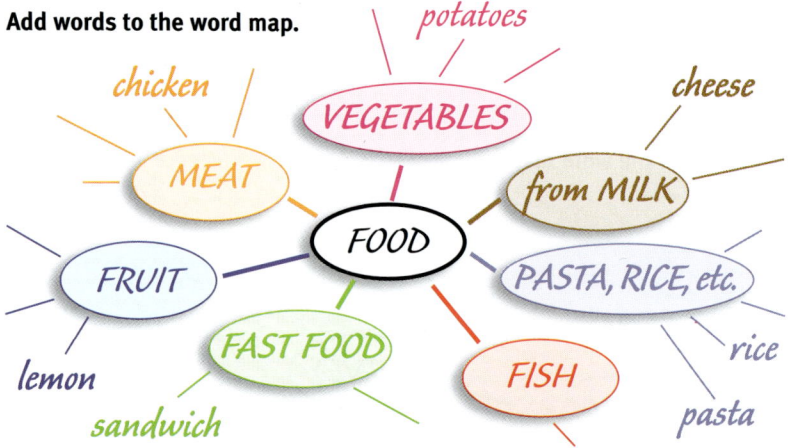

People
Complete the table.

Singular	Plural
man	
	women
child	
baby	
boy	
girl	girls
person	

How many words? (1)

How many words can you find? Use each letter once.

There is one nine-letter word.

P	E	R
N	T	A
A	M	T

20 words = good
30 words = excellent

WORD GAMES

The body

Match the clothes in column A with the correct part of the body in column B.

A	B
shoe	legs
sunglasses	head
hat	hand
trousers	foot
glove	eyes

What are these things?

Add a word from column A to a word or words from column B to make new words, e.g. *handbag*

A	B
hand	chair
arm	phones
head	organ (= harmonica)
foot	bag
mouth	ball
	writing
	band

-ing forms

Look at these song titles. Underline the words ending with *-ing / -in'*.

	SONG	ARTIST
A 1	Feelin' alright	Traffic
B 1	Dancing In The Dark	Bruce Springsteen
A 2	Working In The Coalmine	Lee Dorsey
B 2	Knowing Me, Knowing You	ABBA
A 3	Running Up That Hill	Kate Bush
B 3	Can't Help Falling In Love	Elvis Presley
A 4	Sailing	Rod Stewart
B 4	Having A Good Time	Paul Simon
A 5	Playing In The Band	The Grateful Dead
B 5	Crying	Roy Orbison and k. d. lang
A 6	Kissing A Fool	George Michael
B 6	Going Home	Santana
A 7	Driving Home For Christmas	Chris Rea
B 7	Being With You	Smokey Robinson

How many words? (2)

**How many words can you find? Use each letter once.
There is one nine-letter word.**

O	I	F
Y	D	E
N	B	R

10 words = good

16 words = excellent

Which word? (1)

**Which words do you think of first? Tick (✔) one example.
(All the words are correct.)**

post	☐ postman ☐ post box ☐ post office ☐ postwoman
tea	☐ teapot ☐ tea bag ☐ tea party ☐ cup of tea
office	☐ office desk ☐ office worker ☐ office party ☐ office hours
station	☐ railway station ☐ bus station ☐ fire station ☐ police station
taxi	☐ taxi rank ☐ taxi driver ☐ taxi cab ☐ taxi meter
computer	☐ computer problems ☐ computer program ☐ computer monitor ☐ computer operator

Occupations (1)

Match the occupations in column A with the words in column B.

A	B
mechanic	patient
businessman	car
film star	jumbo jet
journalist	briefcase
nurse	sunglasses
waiter	university
flight attendant	notebook
student	customer

Occupations (2)

Here are some mistakes from newspapers. Find the wrong words. What are the correct words?

He is a famous book, and he has his own TV programme, Cook with Gary on

Two polite officers were with the President, and they stopped the assassin before she

The fight attendants were very courageous and everyone left the Boeing 747 safely

because office wakers are tired after six hours in front of a computer

There are thirty-seven puppies in the average primary school class.

British doctors each have between 2,500 and 3,500 payments to look after, and they

At the end of the meal, the way to brought us chocolate cake and

a Japanese busy man from Sony was in

in hospitals, where purses are working more than fifty hours per week

The daughters performed a heart transplant at St Mary's Hospital in

Transport

Can you find twelve types of transport?

```
G B O A T C B E
A L B U S H I P
T R U C K M C M
R P L A N E Y O
A S Z R T H C P
I V D V A N L E
N J E T X J E D
K Q W O I B N F
```

Irregular past

Change one letter and make these verbs past tense.
come   get   drink   write   win   lose

Add one letter and make these verbs past tense.
move   like   love   hate

Add two letters and make these verbs past tense.
pull   start   finish   work   want   pass   learn

Computers

Circle the correct spellings.

keybord	keybaord	keyboard
scaner	scanner	skanner
modem	moderm	modeme
lapptop	lapttop	laptop
mowse	mouse	muose
cabel	cabal	cable
moniter	monitar	monitor
joystik	joystick	joystic
computer	computre	commputer
printor	printre	printer

Which words are the same in your language?

Which word? (2)

**Which words do you think of first? Tick (✔) one example.
(All the words are correct.)**

play	☐ play football	☐ play the piano	☐ play chess	☐ play a CD
work	☐ work in an office	☐ work at home	☐ homework	☐ work late
live	☐ live at	☐ live in	☐ live with	☐ live for
love	☐ I love you	☐ love letter	☐ love doing (something)	☐ love story
win	☐ win a game	☐ win the lottery	☐ win some money	☐ win the war
go	☐ go to work	☐ go home	☐ go on a diet	☐ go to bed

WORD GAMES

Past verbs

Circle the correct spellings.

went	wenet	wend
bort	buoght	bought
sore	saw	sor
boren	bawn	born
studied	studyed	studdied
stoped	stopped	stopet
movved	moved	movied
marryed	maried	married

How many words? (3)

How many words can you find? Use each letter once.

There is one nine-letter word.

15 words = good
25 words = excellent

Which word? (3)

**Which words do you think of first? Tick (✔) one example.
(All the words are correct.)**

weather	☐ weather report ☐ weather news ☐ weather forecast ☐ weather map
birthday	☐ birthday present ☐ birthday party ☐ birthday cake ☐ Happy Birthday
business	☐ businessman ☐ business meeting ☐ businesswoman ☐ business hours
day	☐ weekday ☐ yesterday ☐ the next day ☐ day ticket
film	☐ film star ☐ 35-mm film ☐ film music ☐ film magazine
bus	☐ bus stop ☐ bus ticket ☐ bus driver ☐ bus company

Opposites: prepositions

Match the prepositions in column A with their opposites in column B.

A	B
in	from
up	across
on	down
to	out
along	off

Sport and exercise
Circle the correct spellings.

climing   climeing   climbing
swimming   swiming   swimeing
exerciseing   exercising   exercizing
cycling   cycleing   cyclling
playying   pleying   playing
runing   running   runeing
weight-training   weight-trainning   weight-treining
ridding   riding   rideing
sking   skkiing   skiing
takeing   takking   taking

On the table
1 **Find the words, e.g.** FINEK *knife*

WOBL   NOPSO   GUM   PUC   GJU   YART
SSAGL   TAPLE   ROFK   TELOBT   PEATOT

2 **Put the words in the correct columns.**

Things you eat with	Things you put food on/in	Things you put drinks in	Things you drink from
spoon	*bowl*	*jug*	*mug*

Leisure (1)
Match words from column A and column B.

A	B
playing	the Internet
watching	the cinema
taking	out
surfing	chess
eating	exercise
going to	television

Animals

1 Circle the different word in each line.

lobster	dog	fish	shrimp
cat	chicken	duck	turkey
cow	sheep	pig	snake
bee	spider	horse	fly
fish	mouse	bird	insect

2 Put the animals in the correct columns.

No feet	Two feet	Four feet	More than four feet

3 Put the animals on the word map. Can you add more food items?

4 Put the words into four lists.

1 Things you can find in your house
2 Things you can find in your garden / street
3 Things you eat
4 Things you kill

Gardens

What can you find in a garden? Complete with these words.

birds   flowers   vegetables   grass   trees   plants

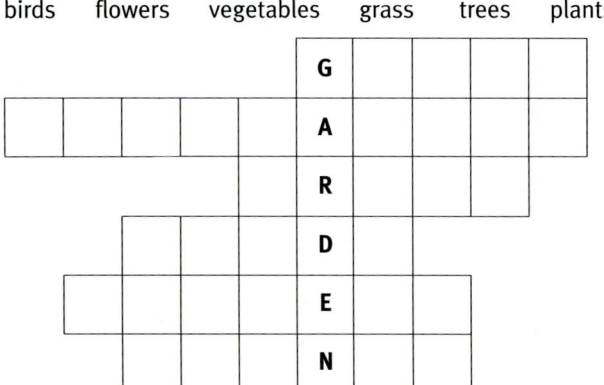

Outdoors

Complete. (Think: singular or plural?)

1 Everest and Kilimanjaro are ....
2 Superior, Michigan, and Ontario are .... in North America.
3 The Amazon and The Mississippi are ....
4 The Mediterranean and Caribbean are ....
5 Copacabana is a famous .... in Rio de Janeiro.
6 There are large evergreen .... in Canada and Russia.

Past participles

Underline the past participles in these song titles.

Leisure (2)

Can you find ten leisure activities?

G	N	H	S	U	R	F	I	N	G
A	C	I	N	G	E	L	N	S	C
R	I	N	G	Z	A	N	G	H	O
D	V	Q	W	T	D	J	M	O	O
E	D	A	N	C	I	N	G	P	K
N	E	A	T	I	N	G	Y	P	I
I	I	N	G	P	G	R	K	I	N
N	X	A	R	U	N	N	I	N	G
G	D	P	L	A	Y	I	N	G	E
G	W	A	L	K	I	N	G	B	R

How many words? (4)

How many words can you find? Use each letter once.

There is one nine-letter word.

D	D	A
Y	W	E
E	S	N

12 words = good

20 words = excellent

Entertainment

Circle the different word in each line.

guitarist	drummer	violinist	pianist
rock	jazz	composer	blues
theatre	dancing	cinema	concert hall
audience	actor	producer	director
DVD	MP3	music	CD

KEY: Word games

Numbers

1 The (Ten) Commandments
2 (Twelfth) Night
3 (Forty-Second) Street
4 (Forty-Eight) Hours
5 The (Forty-Ninth) Parallel
6 (First) Knight
7 The (Seventh) Voyage of Sinbad
8 The (Three) Worlds of Gulliver
9 The (Two-Thousand)-Year-Old Man
10 (Five) Days One Summer

Languages

Italy, Colombia, Scotland, Greece, China, Turkey

Odd one out

cold, shirt, mini-bar, shorts, fish

Food (1)

butter sugar salt pepper peas
tomato potato orange strawberry popcorn
nachos cake chocolate donut toast

Songs

Don't Stop
Don't Worry, Be Happy
Don't Go Near The Water
Be My Baby
Don't Be Cruel
Don't Think Twice, It's Alright
Don't Cry For Me, Argentina
Don't Look Now
Don't Be Angry
Baby Please Don't Go

Money

Student's own answers

Male or female?

1 Charley's (Aunt)
2 (Lord) Of The Rings
3 The (Lady) And The Tramp
4 (Batman) Forever
5 O (Brother), Where Art Thou?
6 (Mrs) Doubtfire
7 (Prince) Of Egypt
8 The General's (Daughter)
9 The (Man) Who Wasn't There
10 The (Princess) (Bride)

Food (2)

salad, lemon, cheese, potato, cake, donut

Food (3)

Student's own answers

People

man / men, woman / women, child / children, baby / babies, boy / boys, girl / girls, person / people

How many words? (1)

apartment (9), a, an, ant, arm, art, at, ate, earn, eat, man, mane, mare, mat, mate, matter, meat, men, name, parent, part, patter, pear, peat, pram, rate, ream, tame, tan, tap, tape, tart, team, ten, term, tram, tramp, trap, treat

The body

shoe / foot, sunglasses / eyes, hat / head, trousers / legs, glove / hand

What are these things?

handbag, hand-ball, handwriting, armchair, armband, headphones, headband, football, mouth-organ

WORD GAMES

-ing forms

A1 <u>Feelin'</u> Alright
B1 <u>Dancing</u> In The Dark
A2 <u>Working</u> In The Coalmine
B2 <u>Knowing</u> Me, <u>Knowing</u> You
A3 <u>Running</u> Up That Hill
B3 Can't Help <u>Falling</u> In Love
A4 <u>Sailing</u>
B4 <u>Having</u> A Good Time
A5 <u>Playing</u> In The Band
B5 <u>Crying</u>
A6 <u>Kissing</u> A Fool
B6 <u>Going</u> Home
A7 <u>Driving</u> Home For Christmas
B7 <u>Being</u> With You

How many words? (2)

boyfriend (9), bend, bind, body, bond, bone, bore, born, boy, brine, den, die, dine, dry, end, fiend, fin, find, fine, fire, for, ford, friend, fry, in, on, one, ride, rode

Which word? (1)

Student's own answers

Occupations (1)

mechanic / car, businessman / briefcase, film star / sunglasses, journalist / notebook, nurse / patient, waiter / customer, flight attendant / jumbo jet, student / university

Occupations (2)

✗ – book	✓ – cook
✗ – polite	✓ – police
✗ – fight	✓ – flight
✗ – wakers	✓ – workers
✗ – puppies	✓ – pupils
✗ – payments	✓ – patients
✗ – way to	✓ – waiter
✗ – busy man	✓ – businessman
✗ – purses	✓ – nurses
✗ – daughters	✓ – doctors

Transport

bicycle, boat, bus, car, jet, moped, plane, ship, taxi, train, truck, van

Irregular past

came, got, drank, wrote, won, lost moved, liked, loved, hated
pulled, started, finished, worked, wanted, passed, learned

Computers

keyboard, scanner, modem, laptop, mouse, cable, monitor, joystick, computer, printer

Which words are the same in your language?

Student's own answers

Which word? (2)

Student's own answers

Past verbs

went, bought, saw, born, studied, stopped, moved, married

How many words? (3)

operation (9), a, an, ant, ape, are, art, at, ate, in, inter, neat, not, on, pain, pair, pane, part, pat, pear, peat, pie, pin, pine, pint, point, port, pot, rain, rate, ration, rip, ripe, rope, root, rot, tap, tape, tear, tin, tip, tone, top, torn, train, trap, trip, troop

Which word? (3)

Student's own answers

Opposites: prepositions

in / out, up / down, on / off, to / from, along / across

Sport and exercise

climbing, swimming, exercising, cycling, playing, running, weight-training, riding, skiing, taking

On the table

bowl spoon mug cup jug tray
glass plate fork bottle teapot

Things you eat with: spoon, fork, knife
Things you put food on/in: bowl, tray, plate
Things you put drinks in: jug, bottle, teapot
Things you drink from: mug, cup, glass

Leisure (1)

playing chess
watching television
taking exercise
surfing the Internet
eating out
going to the cinema

Animals

1. dog, cat, snake, horse, mouse
2. **No feet:** fish, snake
   Two feet: chicken, duck, turkey, bird
   Four feet: dog, cat, cow, sheep, pig, horse, mouse
   More than four feet: lobster, shrimp, spider, fly, bee, insect
3. Student's own answers
4. Sample answers
   1. dog, fish, cat, spider, fly, mouse
   2. dog, cat, bee, spider, fly, mouse, bird, insect
   3. lobster, fish, shrimp, chicken, duck, turkey, cow, sheep, pig
   4. snake, spider, fly, insect

Gardens

GRASS
VEGETABLES
TREES
BIRDS
FLOWERS
PLANTS

Outdoors

1. mountains
2. lakes
3. rivers
4. seas
5. beach
6. forests

Past participles

01 Where Have All The Flowers <u>Gone</u>?
02 Have You <u>Seen</u> Her?
03 She's <u>Gone</u>
04 Have You Ever <u>Been</u> Lonely?
05 I've Just <u>Seen</u> A Face
06 <u>Gone</u>, <u>Gone</u>, Gone
07 We've Only Just <u>Begun</u>
08 <u>Born</u> In The USA
09 I've <u>Lost</u> You
10 We've <u>Found</u> Love

Leisure (2)

cooking, dancing, eating, gardening, playing, reading, running, shopping, surfing, walking

How many words? (4)

Wednesday (9), a, add, an, and, day, days, dew, need, needs, new, news, sad, sadden, sand, saw, sawn, say, see, seed, send, sew, sewed, sewn, wand, wend, was, way, ways, we, wed, weed, yes

Entertainment

drummer, composer, dancing, audience, music

Picture dictionary

Essentials 20
Mathematics 21
Roles 22
Post, mail 23
Routines 24
Things you carry 25
Landscape 26
Actions 27
Uncountables 28
Personal 29
The body 30
Abilities 31
Describing people 32
Clothes, colours 33
Animals 34
Garden 35
Stories 36
On screen 37
Buildings 38
Musical instruments 39
Space 40
Cars 41
Bedroom 42
Kitchen 43

Essentials

Emergency

1 2 3 4

Hospitals, toilets

5 6, 7 8 9 10

Signs

11 12 13 14

Mathematics

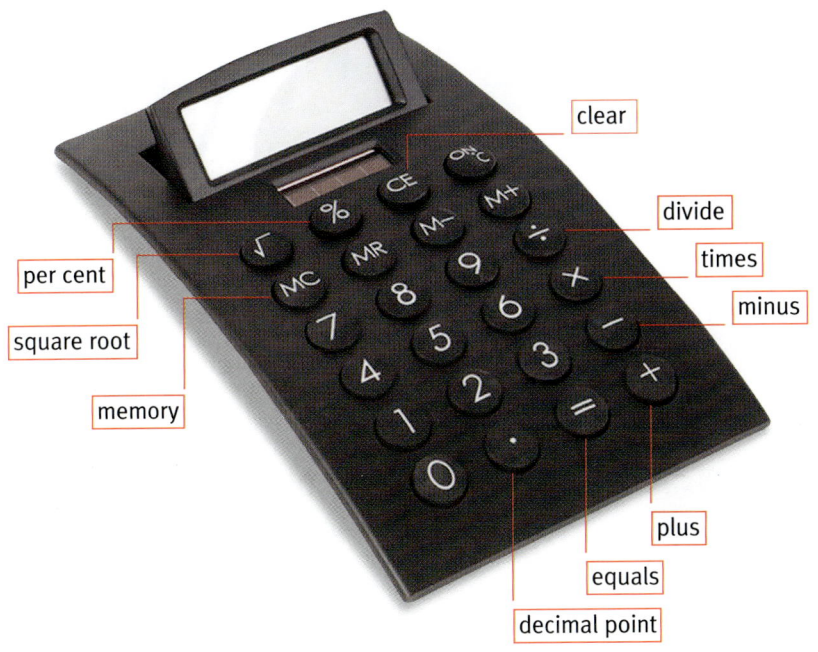

- clear
- divide
- times
- minus
- plus
- equals
- decimal point
- per cent
- square root
- memory

2 + 3 = 5	two plus three equals five
4 − 3 = 1	four minus three equals one
4 x 5 = 20	four times five equals twenty / four multiplied by five equals twenty
24 ÷ 3 = 8	twenty four divided by three equals eight

Large numbers

200	two hundred		250	two hundred and fifty
5,000	five thousand		5,600	five thousand six hundred
6,000,000	six million		100,000	one hundred thousand

Decimals

4.5	four point five
1.6	one point six
9.1	nine point one

Fractions

1/4	quarter
1/2	half
1/3	third
3/4	three quarters
2/3	two thirds

Ordinal numbers

1st	first
2nd	second
3rd	third
4th	fourth
5th	fifth
12th	twelfth

Roles

PICTURE DICTIONARY

Post, mail

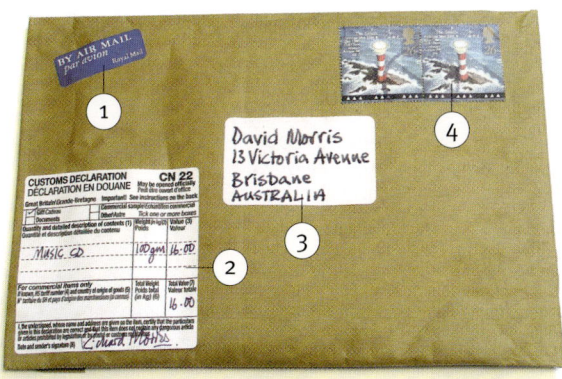

1
2
3
4
5

6
7
8

9
10
11

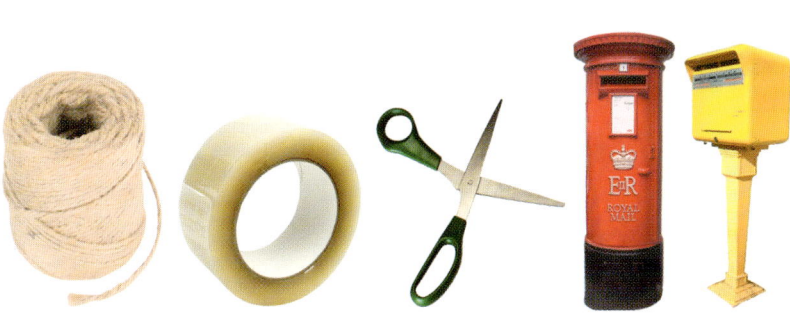

12
13
14
15

Routines

Things you carry

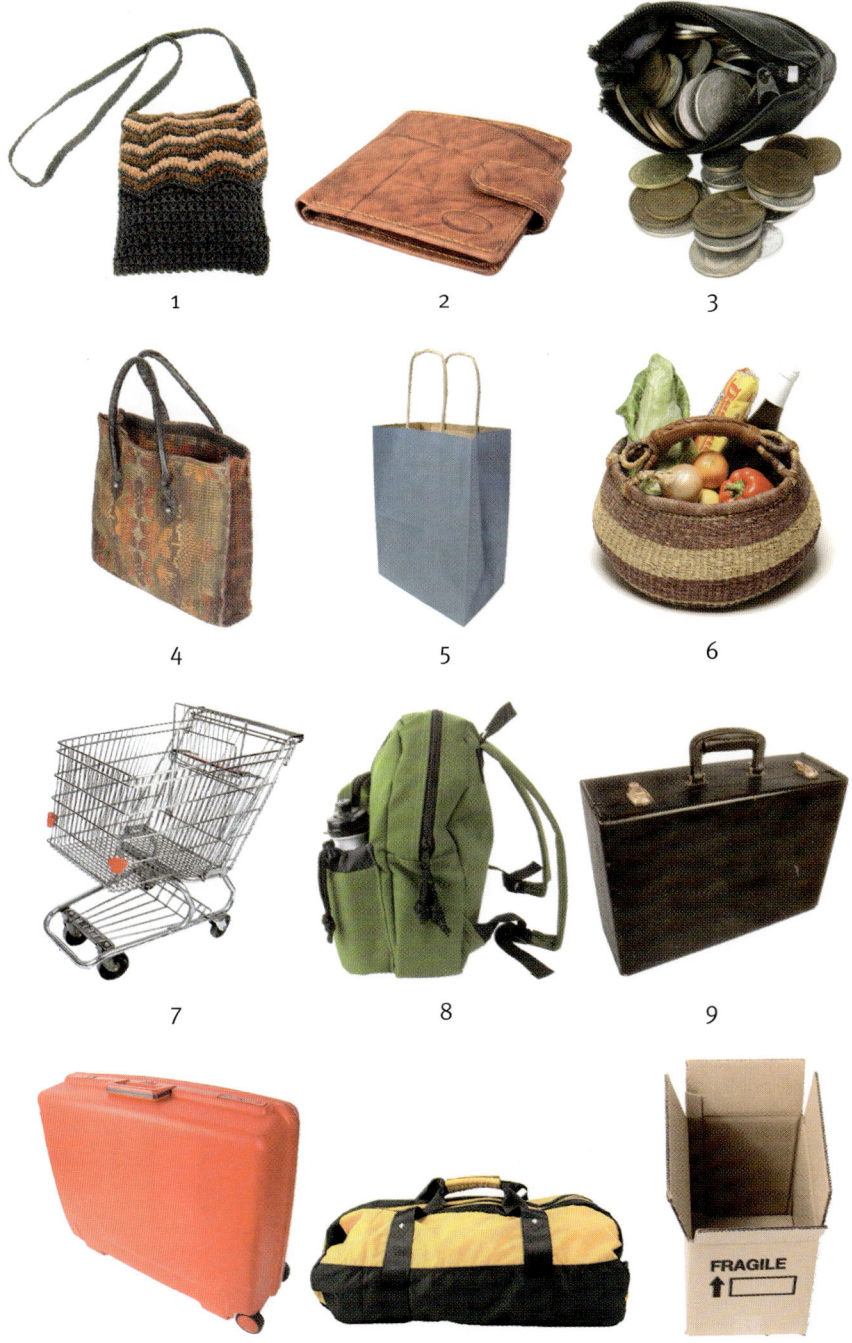

Landscape

1

2, 3

4

5

6, 7

8, 9

10, 11

12

13

14

15

16

PICTURE DICTIONARY

Actions

Uncountables

Liquid

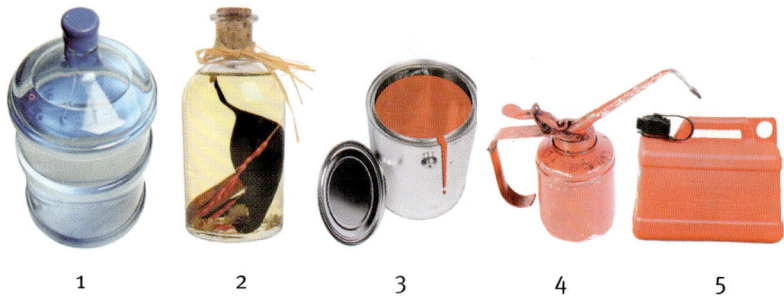

1 2 3 4 5

Gas

6 7 8 9

Solid

10 11 12 13

Food

14 15 16 17 18

Personal

Cleaning teeth, washing

1,2 3 4 5 6

Shaving

7 8 9 10

Hair **First-aid**

11 12 13 14

Paper, towels

15 16 17

Cosmetics, make-up

18 19 20 21 22

The body

PICTURE DICTIONARY

Abilities

Describing people

Clothes, colours

Animals

Farm animals

1
2
3

Pets

4
5
6
7

Birds

8
9
10
11

Reptile **Insects**

12
13
14
15

Fish

16
17
18

Garden

Stories

Fiction

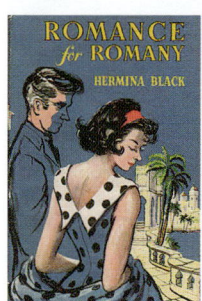
1

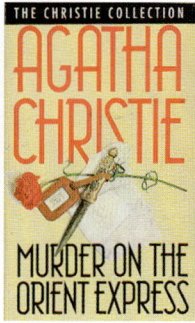
2

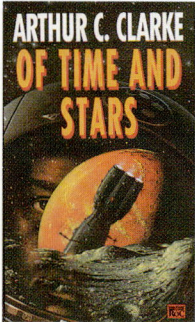
3

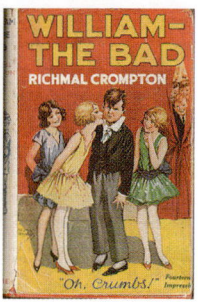
4

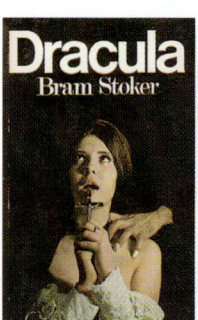
5

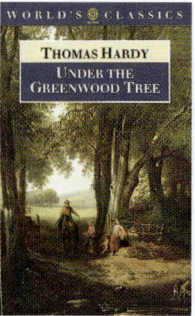
6

7

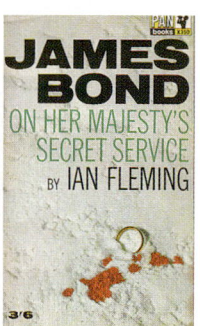
8

Non-fiction

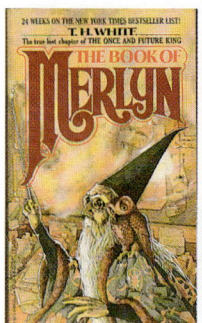
9

10

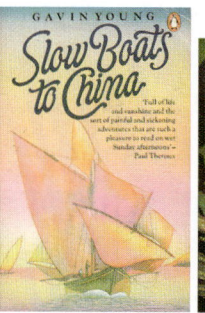
11

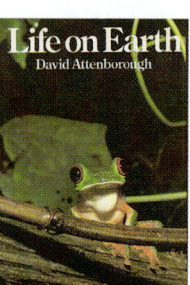
12

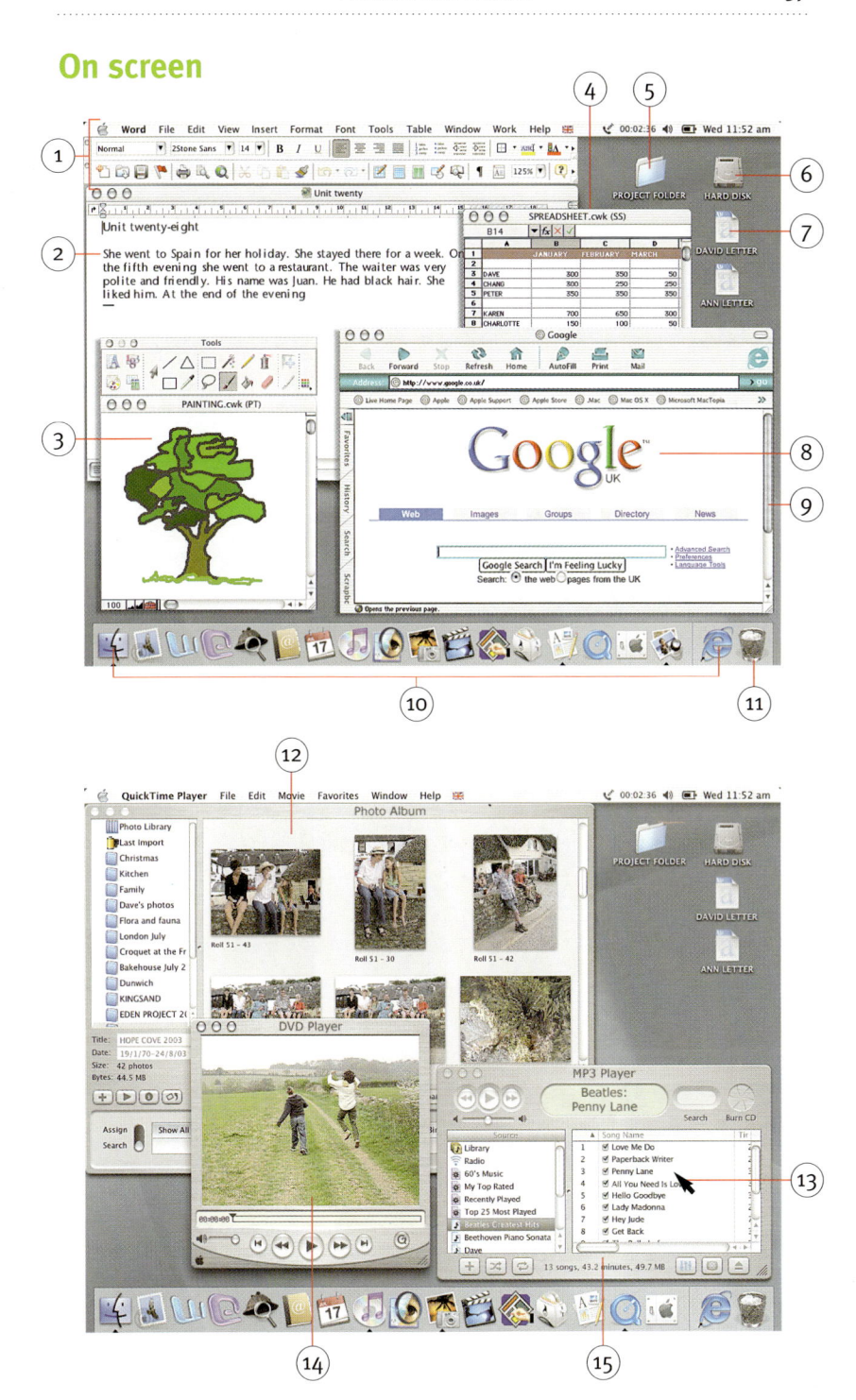

PICTURE DICTIONARY

On screen

Buildings

Houses

Large buildings, architecture

14, 15   16   17   18

Musical instruments

1
2
3
4
5
6
7
8
9
10
11
12
13
14
15

Space

The Solar System

The Sun is a star. The planets go around the Sun. Moons go around the planets.

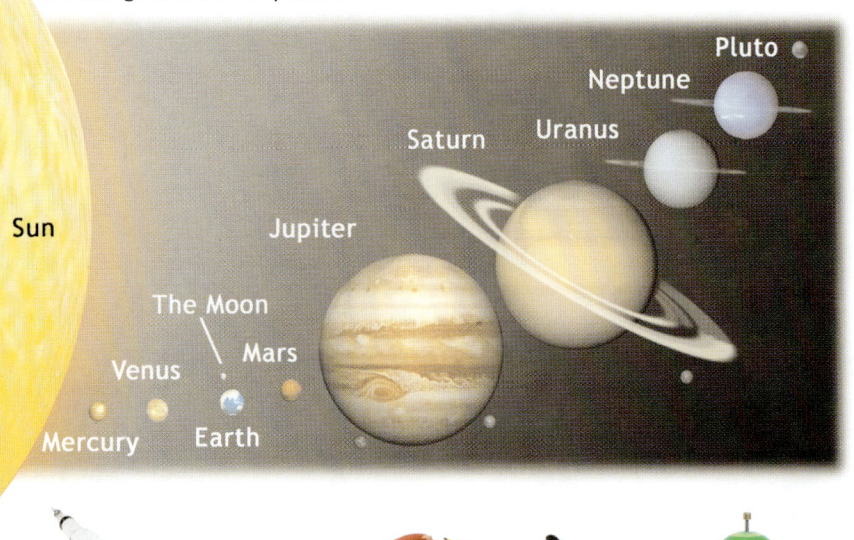

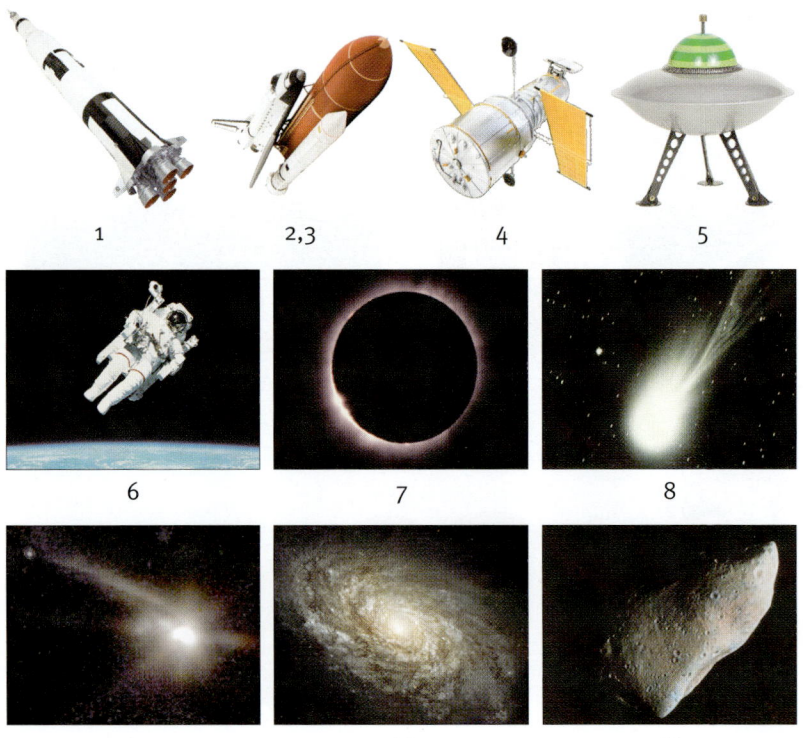

Sun, Mercury, Venus, Earth, The Moon, Mars, Jupiter, Saturn, Uranus, Neptune, Pluto

1
2,3
4
5
6
7
8
9
10
11

/ PICTURE DICTIONARY 41

Cars

Interior

Exterior

PICTURE DICTIONARY

Bedroom

PICTURE DICTIONARY

Kitchen

1
2
3
4
5
6
7
8
9
10
11
12
13
14
15

KEY: Picture dictionary

The words in blue are in the International Phonetic Alphabet. There are 26 letters in the English alphabet, but there are 46 sounds.

Sounds

Vowels

iː	see	/siː/		ʌ	cup	/kʌp/
i	happy	/ˈhæpi/		ɜː	third	/θɜːd/
ɪ	sit	/sɪt/		ə	about	/əˈbaʊt/
e	ten	/ten/		eɪ	day	/deɪ/
æ	hat	/hæt/		əʊ	go	/gəʊ/
ɑː	father	/ˈfɑːðə(r)/		aɪ	five	/faɪv/
ɒ	got	/gɒt/		aʊ	now	/naʊ/
ɔː	four	/fɔː(r)/		ɔɪ	boy	/bɔɪ/
ʊ	foot	/fʊt/		ɪə	near	/nɪə(r)/
u	situation	/sɪtʃuˈeɪʃn/		eə	pair	/peə(r)/
uː	too	/tuː/		ʊə	tourist	/ˈtʊərɪst/

Consonants

p	pen	/pen/		s	so	/səʊ/
b	bad	/bæd/		z	zoo	/zuː/
t	tea	/tiː/		ʃ	shoe	/ʃuː/
d	do	/duː/		ʒ	television	/telɪˈvɪʒn/
k	cat	/kæt/		h	had	/hæd/
g	got	/gɒt/		m	man	/mæn/
tʃ	chair	/tʃeə(r)/		n	no	/nəʊ/
dʒ	June	/dʒuːn/		ŋ	sing	/sɪŋ/
f	five	/faɪv/		l	left	/left/
v	van	/væn/		r	red	/red/
θ	thank	/θænk/		j	yes	/jes/
ð	this	/ðɪs/		w	we	/wiː/

KEY: PICTURE DICTIONARY

Essentials

1. telephone box, payphone /ˈtelɪfəʊn ˌbɒks/ /ˈpeɪfəʊn/
2. police /pəˈliːs/
3. fire /faɪə(r)/
4. ambulance /ˈæmbjələns/
5. hospital /ˈhɒspɪtl/
6. toilets, rest rooms, WCs /ˈtɔɪləts/ /ˈrest ˌruːmz/ /ˌdʌblju: ˈsiːz/
7. disabled, handicapped /dɪsˈeɪbld/ /ˈhændikæpt/
8. women, ladies /ˈwɪmɪn/ /ˈleɪdiːz/
9. men, gentlemen /men/ /ˈdʒentlmən/
10. first aid, first-aid kit, first-aid box /fɜːst ˈeɪd/ /kɪt/ /bɒks/
11. entrance, way in /ˈentrəns/ /ˌweɪ ˈɪn/
12. exit, way out /ˈeksɪt/ /ˌweɪ ˈaʊt/
13. information /ˌɪnfəˈmeɪʃn/
14. danger! /ˈdeɪndʒə(r)/

Mathematics (no key)

Roles

We all have roles. Maybe you're a mother, a dog owner, a driver, an office worker, an employee, a tennis player, and a singer. Only one of these roles is a 'job'.

1. tourists /ˈtʊərɪsts/
2. singer /ˈsɪŋə(r)/
3. runner, winner /ˈrʌnə(r)/ /ˈwɪnə(r)/
4. patient /ˈpeɪʃnt/
5. doctor /ˈdɒktə(r)/
6. traveller, businessman /ˈtrævələ(r)/ /ˈbɪznɪsmæn/
7. bride, wife /braɪd/ /waɪf/
8. groom, husband /gruːm/ /ˈhʌzbənd/
9. police officer /pəˈliːs ˌɒfɪsə(r)/
10. customer, shopper /ˈkʌstəmə(r)/ /ˈʃɒpə(r)/
11. player /ˈpleɪə(r)/
12. factory worker (and an employee of his company) /ˈfæktri ˌwɜːkə(r)/
13. farm worker (and an employee of his boss, the farmer) /ˈfɑːm ˌwɜːkə(r)/
14. office worker (and an employee of her company) /ˈɒfɪs ˌwɜːkə(r)/
15. nurse, hospital worker /nɜːs/
16. driver /ˈdraɪvə(r)/
17. photographer /fəˈtɒgrəfə(r)/
18. (dog) owner /ˈdɒg ˌəʊnə(r)/

Post, mail

1. air-mail sticker /ˈeə(r) meɪl ˌstɪkə(r)/
2. customs form /ˈkʌstəmz fɔːm/
3. label, address label /ˈleɪbl/ /əˈdres ˌleɪbl/
4. stamps (stick a stamp on a letter) /stæmps/
5. postcard /ˈpəʊst ˌkɑːd/
6. envelopes /ˈenvələʊps/
7. sticker /ˈstɪkə(r)/
8. greetings card /ˈgriːtɪŋz ˌkɑːd/
9. letters /ˈletə(r)z/
10. packet, package /ˈpækɪt/ /ˈpækɪdʒ/
11. parcel /ˈpɑːsl/
12. string (tie with string) /strɪŋ/
13. sellotape (UK) /ˈseləteɪp/ Scotch tape (US) /ˈskɒtʃ ˌteɪp/ (stick with sellotape)
14. scissors (cut with scissors) /ˈsɪzəz/
15. postbox (UK) /ˈpəʊstbɒks/ mailbox (US) /ˈmeɪlbɒks/

Routines

Routines are things you do every day.

1. clean / brush your teeth /kliːn jɔː(r)tiːθ/ /brʌʃ/
2. wash, wash your face, have a wash /wɒʃ/ /wɒʃ jɔː(r) feɪs/ /hæv ə wɒʃ/
3. wash your hair /wɒʃ jɔː(r) heə(r)/
4. brush your hair /brʌʃ jɔː(r) heə(r)/
5. have / take a bath (or have / take a shower) /hæv ə bɑːθ/ /teɪk ə ʃaʊə(r)/
6. cook, prepare a meal, make dinner /kʊk/ /prəˌpeə(r) ə ˈmiːl/ /meɪk ˈdɪnə(r)/
7. have breakfast /hæv ˈbrekfəst/
8. have lunch /hæv lʌntʃ/
9. have dinner /hæv ˈdɪnə(r)/
10. eat /iːt/
11. drink (wine) /drɪŋk waɪn/
12. do exercise, take exercise, work out (US) /duː eksəsaɪz/ /teɪk/ /ˌwɜːk ˈaʊt/
13. work /wɜːk/
14. read /riːd/
15. study /ˈstʌdi/
16. watch TV /wɒtʃ tiː ˈviː/
17. play with children /ˈpleɪ wɪð ˈtʃɪldrən/
18. sleep, go to bed /sliːp/ /gəʊ tə bed/

KEY: PICTURE DICTIONARY

Things you carry

1. handbag (UK) /'hændbæg/
   purse (US) /pɜː(r)s/
2. wallet (UK) /'wɒlɪt/
   billfold (US) /'bɪlfəʊld/
3. purse (UK, US) /pɜː(r)s/
   wallet (US) /'wɒlət/
4. bag /bæɡ/
5. shopping bag, carrier bag /'ʃɒpɪŋ bæɡ/ /'kæriə(r) bæɡ/
6. basket, shopping basket /bɑːskɪt/ /'ʃɒpɪŋ ˌbɑːskɪt/
7. trolley (UK) /'trɒli/
   shopping cart (US) /'ʃɒpɪŋ kɑː(r)t/
8. backpack /'bækpæk/
9. briefcase /'briːfkeɪs/
10. luggage; suitcase /'lʌɡɪdʒ/ /'suːtkeɪs/
11. luggage; bag, holdall /'lʌɡɪdʒ/ /bæɡ/ /'həʊldɔːl/
12. box, cardboard box /bɒks/ /'kɑːdbɔːd bɒks/

Landscape

1. hill /hɪl/
2. mountain /'maʊntən/
3. lake /leɪk/
4. valley /'væli/
5. cliffs /klɪfs/
6. country, countryside /'kʌntri/ /'kʌntrisaɪd/
7. fields /fiːldz/
8. bridge /brɪdʒ/
9. river /'rɪvə(r)/
10. rocks /'rɒks/
11. sea (UK), ocean (US) /siː/ /'əʊʃən/
12. beach /biːtʃ/
13. desert /'dezə(r)t/
14. wood (small), forest (big) /wʊd/ /'fɒrɪst/
15. island /'aɪlənd/
16. waterfall /'wɔːtəfɔːl/

Actions

1. walking /'wɔːkɪŋ/
2. running /'rʌnɪŋ/
3. waiting /'weɪtɪŋ/
4. sitting /'sɪtɪŋ/
5. standing /'stændɪŋ/
6. climbing (a ladder) /'klaɪmɪŋ ə ˌlædə(r)/
7. picking up (the paper), giving (the paper) to her /'pɪkɪŋ ʌp ðə ˌpeɪpə(r)/ /'ɡɪvɪŋ ðə ˌpeɪpə(r) tə hɜː(r)/
8. throwing /'θrəʊɪŋ/
9. catching /'kætʃɪŋ/
10. kissing /'kɪsɪŋ/
11. falling (over) /'fɔːlɪŋ ˌəʊvə(r)/
12. fighting /'faɪtɪŋ/
13. flying /'flaɪɪŋ/
14. jumping /'dʒʌmpɪŋ/
15. kicking /'kɪkɪŋ/
16. hitting /'hɪtɪŋ/
17. pushing /'pʊʃɪŋ/

Uncountables

1. water /'wɔːtə(r)/
2. oil, cooking oil /ɔɪl/ /'kʊkɪŋ ɔɪl/
3. paint /peɪnt/
4. oil, motor oil /ɔɪl/ /'məʊtə(r) ɔɪl/
5. petrol (UK) /'petrəl/
   gas / gasoline (US) /ɡæs/ /'ɡæsəliːn/
6. air (inside a hot-air balloon) /eə(r)/
7. smoke /sməʊk/
8. gas /ɡæs/
9. oxygen (O2) /'ɒksɪdʒən/
10. sand /sænd/
11. dirt, soil, earth /dɜːt/ /sɔɪl/ /ɜːθ/
12. rock /rɒk/
13. ice /aɪs/
14. cheese /tʃiːz/
15. bread /bred/
16. rice /raɪs/
17. sweetcorn (UK) /'swiːtkɔːn/
    corn (US) /kɔːn/
18. spaghetti /spə'ɡeti/

Personal

[C] = countable, [U] = uncountable

1. toothbrush [C] /'tuːθbrʌʃ/
2. toothpaste [U] /'tuːθpeɪst/
3. soap [U] /səʊp/
4. nail brush [C] /neɪl brʌʃ/
5. handwash [U] /'hændwɒʃ/
6. shampoo (for your hair) [U] /ʃæm'puː/
7. shaver, electric shaver [C] /'ʃeɪvə(r)/ /ɪ'lektrɪk ˌʃeɪvə(r)/
8. razor [C] /'reɪzə(r)/
9. after-shave, cologne [U] /'ɑːftə(r) ˌʃeɪv/
10. mirror [C] /'mɪrə(r)/

11 comb [C] /kəʊm/
12 hairbrush [C] /ˈheə(r) brʌʃ/
13 bandage [C] /ˈbændɪdʒ/
14 plaster (UK) /ˈplɑːstə(r)/
   Band-aid (US, UK) [C] /ˈbænd ˌeɪd/
15 tissues (UK), Kleenex (US)
   /ˈtɪʃuːz/ /ˈkliːneks/
   paper hankies (UK) [C]
   /ˌpeɪpə(r) ˈhæŋkiːz/
16 toilet paper, toilet roll [U]
   /ˈtɔɪlət ˌpeɪpə(r)/
17 towels (also hand towels, bath towels, face towels) [C] /taʊlz/
18 lipstick [C, U] /ˈlɪpstɪk/
19 eye-shadow [U] /ˈaɪ ˌʃædəʊ/
20 face powder [U] /ˈfeɪs ˌpaʊdə(r)/
21 nail polish (US, UK), nail varnish (UK) [U]
   /ˈneɪl ˌpɒlɪʃ/ /ˈneɪl ˌvɑːnɪʃ/
22 perfume [U] /ˈpɜːfjuːm/

The body

1 head /hed/
2 breast (female), chest (male)
  /brest/ /tʃest/
3 stomach /ˈstʌmək/
4 ankle /ˈæŋkl/
5 toes /təʊz/
6 foot /fʊt/
7 leg (calf) /leg/ /kɑːf/
8 leg (thigh) /leg/ /θaɪ/
9 bottom /ˈbɒtəm/
10 back /bæk/
11 hand /hænd/
12 arm /ɑːm/
13 forehead /ˈfɔːhed/
14 eye /aɪ/
15 nose /nəʊz/
16 mouth /maʊθ/
17 shoulder /ˈʃəʊldə(r)/
18 wrist /rɪst/
19 elbow /ˈelbəʊ/
20 waist /weɪst/
21 hip /hɪp/
22 knee /niː/
23 neck /nek/
24 fingers /ˈfɪŋgəz/

Abilities

Can you do these things?

1 type, key in, touch-type (= type with all your fingers) /taɪp/ /ˌkiː ˈɪn/ /ˈtʌtʃ ˌtaɪp/
  (*to key in* is becoming more frequent than *type* for computers)
2 play (chess) /pleɪ ˈtʃes/
3 cook /kʊk/
4 text, send a text message
  /tekst/ /send ə ˈtekst ˌmesɪdʒ/
5 play (the guitar), play guitar
  /pleɪ (ðə) gɪˈtɑː/
6 ride (a bicycle) /ˌraɪd ə ˈbaɪsəkəl/
7 ski /skiː/
8 dive /daɪv/
9 swim /swɪm/
10 drive /draɪv/
11 sew /səʊ/
12 read music /riːd ˈmjuːzɪk/

Describing people

1 Afro-Caribbean, brown eyes, about 30
2 Caucasian, blue eyes, blonde, about 20
3 light brown hair, about 65
4 grey hair, wearing glasses, elderly, about 75
5 Asian, black hair, about 25
6 elderly, grey hair, balding, about 80
7 Hispanic, black hair, moustache and beard, about 28
8 African-American, brown eyes, short hair, about 30
9 Asian, black hair, brown eyes, about 35
10 Caucasian, smart hair, about 25
11 straight hair, black hair, wearing glasses
12 curly hair, long hair, red hair
13 bald, moustache and beard
14 very short hair, wearing earrings, wearing a necklace
15 girl, boy, children, brother and sister, son, daughter
16 woman, man, baby, parents, mother, father, child
17 woman, man, grandparents

Clothes, colours

Clothes

1. swimsuit, bathing costume /ˈswɪmsuːt/ /ˈbeɪθɪŋ ˌkɒstjuːm/
2. shorts (for swimming = swimming trunks) /ʃɔːts/
3. trousers (UK, US), pants (US) /ˈtraʊzəz/ /pænts/
4. shoes /ʃuːz/
5. dress /dres/
6. skirt /skɛːt/
7. top /tɒp/
8. blouse /blaʊz/
9. sweater /ˈswetə(r)/
10. T-shirt /ˈtiː ʃɜːt/
11. sports shirt, short-sleeved shirt /ˈspɔːts ʃɜːt/ /ˌʃɔːt sliːvd ˈʃɜːt/
12. shirt, long-sleeved shirt /ʃɜːt/ /ˌlɒŋ sliːvd ˈʃɜːt/
13. hat /hæt/
14. cap, baseball cap /kæp/ /ˈbeɪsbɔːl kæp/
15. helmet, safety helmet /ˈhelmət/ /ˈseɪfti ˌhelmət/
16. gloves /ɡlʌvz/
17. belt /belt/
18. socks /sɒks/
19. tie /taɪ/
20. scarf /skɑːf/

Colours

1. blue, red, and yellow /bluː/ /red/ /ˈjeləʊ/
2. light blue, cream /ˌlaɪt bluː/ /kriːm/
3. beige, blue /beɪʒ/ /bluː/
4. light brown /ˈlaɪt braʊn/
5. blue (dark blue and light blue) /bluː/ /dɑːk/ /laɪt/
6. white /waɪt/
7. black /blæk/
8. pink /pɪŋk/
9. brown and white /braʊn ən(d) waɪt/
10. red and white /red ən(d) waɪt/
11. light blue, brown and white /laɪt bluː/ /braʊn ən(d) waɪt/
12. grey /ɡreɪ/
13. grey /ɡreɪ/
14. red /red/
15. green /ɡriːn/
16. yellow / tan /ˈjeləʊ/ /tæn/
17. brown /braʊn/
18. light grey /laɪt ɡreɪ/

19. blue, black, and yellow /bluː/ /blæk/ /ˈjeləʊ/
20. yellow and brown /ˈjeləʊ ən(d) braʊn/

Animals

1. pig /pɪɡ/
2. cow /kaʊ/
3. horse /hɔːs/
4. sheep /ʃiːp/
5. mouse /maʊs/
6. cat /kæt/
7. dog /dɒɡ/
8. bird /bɜːd/
9. chicken /ˈtʃɪkɪn/
10. turkey /ˈtɜːki/
11. duck /dʌk/
12. snake /sneɪk/
13. spider /ˈspaɪdə(r)/
A *spider* is an *arachnid*, but is an *insect* in everyday English.
14. bee /biː/
15. fly /flaɪ/
16. fish /fɪʃ/
17. shrimp /ʃrɪmp/
18. lobster /ˈlɒbstə(r)/
Lobster and *shrimp* are *crustaceans*, not *fish*. In a restaurant they're both *sea food*.

Garden

1. plants /plɑːnts/
2. flowers /ˈflaʊəz/
3. herbs /hɜːbz/
4. trees /triːz/
5. bushes, shrubs /ˈbʊʃɪz/ /ʃrʌbz/
6. grass, a lawn /ɡrɑːs/ /ə lɔːn/
7. path /pɑːθ/
8. gate /ɡeɪt/
9. steps /steps/
10. branches /ˈbrɑːntʃɪz/
11. leaves /liːvz/
12. pot, plant pot, pot of (flowers) /pɒt/ /ˈplɑːnt pɒt/ /pɒt əv ˈflaʊəz/

Stories

You can use the same words to describe books or films.

Fiction

1. romance, romantic novel /rəʊˈmæns/ /rəʊˌmæntɪk ˈnɒvl/

KEY: PICTURE DICTIONARY

2 mystery, murder mystery, detective story
/ˈmɪstri/ /ˈmɜːdə(r) ˌmɪstri/
/dɪˈtektɪv ˈstɔːri/
3 sci-fi, science-fiction
/saɪ faɪ/ /ˌsaɪəns ˈfɪkʃn/
4 children's, humour, comedy
/ˈtʃɪldrənz/ /ˈhjuːmə(r)/ /ˈkɒmədi/
5 horror /ˈhɒrə(r)/
6 classic, classic novel
/ˈklæsɪk/ /ˌklæsɪk ˈnɒvl/
7 war, war story /wɔː/ /stɔːri/
8 spy /spaɪ/
9 fantasy /ˈfæntəsi/

Non-fiction

10 biography (about someone else), autobiography (about yourself)
/baɪˈɒɡrəfi/ /ˌɔːtəbaɪˈɒɡrəfi/
11 travel /ˈtrævl/
12 nature, TV tie-in
/ˈneɪtʃə(r)/ /tiː viː ˈtaɪ ɪn/

On screen

1 menu bar, toolbar
/ˈmenjuː bɑː/ /ˈtuːlbɑː/
2 word processor /wɜːd ˈprəʊsesə(r)/
3 illustration program
/ˌɪləˈstreɪʃn ˈprəʊɡræm/
(painting, drawing)
/ˈpeɪntɪŋ/ /ˈdrɔːɪŋ/
4 spreadsheet /ˈspredʃiːt/
5 folder /ˈfəʊldə(r)/
6 hard disk /ˈhɑːd dɪsk/
7 document /ˈdɒkjəmənt/
8 search engine /ˈsɜːtʃ ˌendʒɪn/
9 scroll bar /ˈskrəʊl bɑː(r)/
10 icons (for programs) /ˈaɪkɒnz/
11 trash /træʃ/
12 photo album /ˌfəʊtəʊ ˈælbəm/
13 cursor /ˈkɜːsə(r)/
14 DVD player /diːviːˈdiː ˌpleɪə(r)/
15 MP3 player, CD burner
/empiˈθriː ˌpleɪə(r)/ /siː ˌdiː ˌbɜːnə(r)/

Buildings

1 wall /wɔːl/
2 porch /pɔːtʃ/
3 window /ˈwɪndəʊ/
4 lawn /lɔːn/
5 steps /steps/
6 door, front door /dɔː/ /ˈfrʌnt dɔː/
7 drive (UK), driveway (US)
/draɪv/ /ˈdraɪvweɪ/

8 garage /ˈɡærɑːʒ/
9 roof /ruːf/
10 stairs, staircase
/steə(r)z/ /ˈsteə(r) keɪs/
11 escalator /ˈeskəleɪtə(r)/
12 arch /ɑːtʃ/
13 columns, pillars /ˈkɒləmz/ /ˈpɪləz/
14 tower /ˈtaʊə(r)/
15 dome (on top) /dəʊm/
16 balcony /ˈbælkəni/
17 statue /ˈstætjuː/
18 fountain /ˈfaʊntɪn/

Musical instruments

1 violin /vaɪəˈlɪn/
2 guitar, acoustic guitar
/ɡɪˈtɑː/ /əˈkuːstɪk ɡɪˈtɑː/
3 guitar, electric guitar
/ɡɪˈtɑː/ /ɪˈlektrɪk ɡɪˈtɑː/
4 bass guitar, bass
/beɪs ɡɪˈtɑː/ /beɪs/
5 clarinet /ˌklærɪˈnet/
6 saxophone /ˈsæksəˌfəʊn/
7 trumpet /ˈtrʌmpɪt/
8 trombone /trɒmˈbəʊn/
9 piano, grand piano /piˈænəʊ/
10 organ /ˈɔːɡən/
11 keyboard, synthesizer
/ˈkiːbɔːd/ /ˈsɪnθəsaɪzə/
12 drums /drʌmz/
13 congas /ˈkɒŋɡəz/
14 tambourine /ˌtæmbəˈriːn/
15 triangle /ˈtraɪæŋɡl/

Space

1 rocket /ˈrɒkɪt/
2 space shuttle /ˈspeɪs ˌʃʌtl/
3 launcher /ˈlɔːntʃə(r)/
4 satellite /ˈsætəlaɪt/
5 UFO, flying saucer
/ˌjuːefˈəʊ/ /ˌflaɪŋ ˈsɔːsə(r)/
6 astronaut (USA), cosmonaut (Russia)
/ˈæstrənɔːt/ /ˈkɒzmənɔːt/
7 eclipse /ɪˈklɪps/
8 comet /ˈkɒmɪt/
9 star /stɑː(r)/
10 galaxy /ˈɡæləksi/
11 asteroid /ˈæstərɔɪd/

Cars

Interior
1. speedometer (with odometer / mileometer and trip meter)
   /spiːˈdɒmɪtə(r)/ /əʊˈdɒmɪtə(r)/ /ˈmaɪlɒmɪtə(r)/
2. rev counter, tachometer
   /ˈrev ˌkaʊntə(r)/ /tækˈɒmɪtə(r)/
3. steering wheel /ˈstɪərɪŋ wiːl/
4. clock /klɒk/

Foot pedals
5. accelerator (UK), gas pedal (US)
   /əkˈseləreɪtə(r)/ /ˈgæs pedl/
6. brake /breɪk/
7. clutch (on manual cars) /klʌtʃ/
8. handbrake, parking brake
   /ˈhændbreɪk/ /ˈpɑːkɪŋ breɪk/
9. gear stick, gear lever (UK)
   /ˈgɪə stɪk/
   gear shift, stick shift (US)
   /ˈgɪə ʃɪft/ /ˈstɪk ʃɪft/

Cars are *manual* or *automatic*.

10. heater, air conditioning, automatic climate control
    /ˈhiːtə(r)/ /eə(r) kɒnˈdɪʃnɪŋ/ /ˌɔːtəmætɪk ˈklaɪmət kənˌtrəʊl/
11. radio, CD-player controls /ˈreɪdiəʊ/ /siːˈdiː pleɪə(r) kənˌtrəʊlz/
12. glove compartment
    /ˈglʌv kəmˌpɑːtmənt/
13. vents, ventilation
    /vents/ /ˌventɪˈleɪʃn/

Exterior
1. headrest /ˈhedrest/
2. mirror, exterior mirror
   /ˈmɪrə(r)/ /ɪkˈstɪəriə(r) ˌmɪrə(r)/
3. windscreen (UK), windshield (US)
   /ˈwɪndskriːn/ /ˈwɪndʃiːld/
4. bonnet (UK), hood (US)
   /ˈbɒnɪt/ /hʊd/
5. radiator grill /ˈreɪdieɪtə(r) grɪl/
6. number plate, registration plate
   /ˈnʌmbə(r) pleɪt/ /ˌredʒɪsˈtreɪʃn pleɪt/
7. bumper (UK), fender (US)
   /ˈbʌmpə(r)/ /ˈfendə(r)/
8. headlight, headlamp
   /ˈhedlaɪt/ /ˈhedlæmp/
9. wheel /wiːl/
10. tyre (UK), tire (US) /taɪə/
11. wing /wɪŋ/
12. boot (UK), trunk (US) /buːt/ /trʌŋk/

Bedroom

1. pillow /ˈpɪləʊ/
2. duvet (UK), quilt (US)
   /ˈduːveɪ/ /kwɪlt/
3. sheet /ʃiːt/
4. blanket /ˈblæŋkɪt/
5. pillow (on a bed), cushion (on a chair)
   /ˈpɪləʊ/ /kʊʃn/
6. rug (small), carpet (big)
   /rʌg/ /ˈkɑːpɪt/
7. laundry (UK, US), washing (UK)
   /ˈlɔːndri/ /ˈwɒʃɪŋ/
8. switch /swɪtʃ/
9. socket (UK, US), outlet (US)
   /ˈsɒkɪt/ /ˈaʊtlet/
10. lamp, table-lamp /læmp/ /ˈteɪbl læmp/
11. alarm clock /əˈlɑːm klɒk/
12. bulb, light bulb /bʌlb/ /laɪt bʌlb/
13. taps /tæps/
14. dryer, hair dryer (also drier, hair drier)
    /ˈdraɪə(r)/ /heə ˈdraɪə(r)/
15. bedside table /ˌbedsaɪd ˈteɪbl/

Kitchen

1. bowls /bəʊlz/
2. plates /pleɪts/
3. jug /dʒʌg/
4. cups and saucers
   /kʌps ən(d) ˈsɔːsəz/
5. fork /fɔːk/
6. knife /naɪf/
7. spoon /spuːn/
8. frying pan /ˈfraɪɪŋ pæn/
9. saucepan /ˈsɔːspən/
10. kettle /ˈketl/
11. pots (pans) /pɒts/ /pænz/
12. cooking dish, casserole dish
    /ˈkʊkɪŋ dɪʃ/ /ˈkæsərəʊl dɪʃ/
13. food mixer /ˈfuːd ˌmɪksə(r)/
14. hotplate, burner /ˈhɒtpleɪt/ /ˈbɜːnə(r)/
15. grill /grɪl/

Everyday English

1 Asking for help   53
2 Meeting people   54
3 Lifts   55
4 Taxis   56
5 Thanks   57
6 Public transport   58
7 On the beach   59
8 At the table   60
9 Hotel basics   61
10 Visitors   62
11 Reservations   63
12 Restaurant   64
13 Paying   65
14 Time   66
15 Telephoning   67
16 Telephone messages   68
17 Getting around   69
18 Appointments   70
19 Airport check-in   71
20 Tourism   72
21 On a plane   73
22 At the bank   74

How to use this section

**Inside your *3 in 1 Practice Pack* there is a square of red plastic.
When you cover the text with this square you can read the words in black,
but you can't see the words in pink.**

PINK
BLACK

PI
BLACK

■ = **Put the red plastic square over the conversation.**

Method

1 Read the conversation.
2 ■ Put the red plastic square over the conversation.
3 Complete the conversation. Remember the words in pink.
   Say them to yourself.

EVERYDAY ENGLISH 53

1 Asking for help

- Excuse me?
- Yes?
- Do you speak English?
- Yes. A little.

- Can you translate 'pasta' into English?
- Pasta.
- No. What's 'pasta' in English?
- The same. Pasta.

- Good morning. How can I help you?
- Sorry, can you speak slowly, please?

- Can I help you?
- How much is it?
- Forty-seven fifty-three, including VAT.
- Sorry. Can you repeat that?

■ **Complete the conversations.**

2 Meeting people

- Hello! How are you?
- I'm fine, thanks. And you?
- I'm very well.

- This is David Hudson.
- How do you do?
- How do you do?

- Hey! How's it going?
- Great. How are you doing?
- I'm good.

- Good morning. My name's Owen. Richard Owen.
- Good morning, Mr Owen. How can I help you?

■ **Complete the conversations.**

3 Lifts

- Going up?
- No, sorry. Going down.

- After you.
- Thanks.

- Excuse me.
- Sorry.

- Which floor?
- Twenty-three.

- Do you want the ground floor?
- No, the first floor, please.

- Can you hold the door?
- I've got it.
- Thanks.

■ **Complete the conversations.**

4 Taxis

Excuse me ...
Yes?
Where can I get a taxi?
Right outside the terminal.

Taxi!
Where to?
The Holiday Inn, please.
Which one? The airport or the town centre?
The town centre, please.

Radio cabs?
What name?
Can I have a taxi from 34 High Street, please?
(Smith).

Where to?
The station, please.

■ Complete the conversations.

EVERYDAY ENGLISH 57

5 Thanks

Happy birthday!

These are for you.

Thank you.

They're lovely! That's so kind of you. Thanks.

Would you like another drink?

Yes, please. Thank you.

Wow! Is this for me?

Thank you! What's inside?

Yes, it is. Happy birthday.

Open it and see.

Oh dear! Let me help you.

This is yours ... and this.

Thanks.

Thank you.

■ **Complete the conversations.**

6 Public transport

A Excuse me, is this the platform for the London train?
B No, it isn't. That's the platform over there.
A Which number?
B Platform 3.

A Excuse me, does the number-32 bus stop here?
C No, it doesn't.
A Where does it stop?
C Over there.

A Is this the bus to the town centre?
D Yes, it is.

D Fares, please.
A The town centre, please.
D One twenty.
A Here you are. Can you tell me when we get there?
D Sure.

■ **You are A, the person asking for information. Complete the conversations.**

7   On the beach

A   Two ice-creams, please.
B   What flavour?
A   A strawberry one and a vanilla one.
B   Would you like a chocolate flake with those?
A   No, thanks.

A   Have you got any chocolate ice-cream?
B   Yes, we have.
A   Great. Two, please.
B   There you go.

A   I'd like a cola, please.
B   Regular or large?
A   Regular.
B   Ice and lemon?
A   Just ice. No lemon.

A   How much are the postcards?
B   Thirty-five pence each.
A   These three, please.
B   That's one pound five altogether.
A   Do you sell stamps?
B   Sorry, we don't.

■   **You are A, the customer. Complete the conversations.**

8 At the table

B More wine?
A No, thanks. I'm fine.
B Are you sure?
A Yes, I'm sure. I'm driving.

C Help yourself to salad.
A Thanks, I will.
C And bread.
A Thank you.

A Could you pass the salad dressing?
B Here you are.
A And could I have some pepper?
B Yes, of course.

B Coffee?
A Please.
B Milk and sugar?
A Milk, please. No sugar.

■ **You are A, the guest. Complete the conversations.**

9 Hotel basics

A Is the tap water safe to drink?
B Yes, it's safe. But most people drink bottled water.
A Is there a mini-bar in the room?
B No, but you can get a bottle of water from the bar.

C Housekeeping. How can I help you?
A Can you send an engineer to my room? There's a problem with the toilet.
C That's room 13?
A That's right. How long will it be?
C A couple of minutes.

D Laundry services. How can I help you?
A I've got some laundry in room 13. Can you do it overnight?
D Yes, is it in a hotel bag?
A Yes.
D And have you completed the laundry list?
A Yes. But I'm just going downstairs for dinner.
D That's OK. Please leave the bag on the bed. We'll pick it up later.

B Reception. How can I help you?
A Can I have an alarm-call at five forty-five, please.
B Certainly. Room 13. Five forty-five.
A Thank you. Goodnight.
B Goodnight.

■ **You are A, the hotel guest. Complete the conversations.**

10 Visitors

A Good morning. Can I help you?
B Good morning. I've got an appointment with Mrs Fox.
A What time?
B Eleven o'clock.
A And what's your name?
B Hudson. Angela Hudson.
A Pleased to meet you, Miss Hudson. I'm Mrs Fox's personal assistant, (Sue Reed).
B Pleased to meet you, (Ms Reed).
A Take a seat. Would you like something to drink?
B Oh, yes, I would. Thank you very much.
A Would you like tea or coffee?
B Coffee, please. Have you got any decaffeinated coffee?
A Yes, we have. Would you like milk and sugar?
B Milk, please. No sugar.
A Would you like some biscuits?
B No, thank you.

■ **You are A, the personal assistant. Complete the conversation.**

11 Reservations

A Do I need a reservation for the hotel restaurant?
B It depends. What time?
A Around eight o'clock.
B It's busy then. A reservation's a good idea.

■ **You are A, the customer. Complete the conversation.**

A Can I make a reservation for tonight?
C Certainly. What time?
A Around eight o'clock.
C That's fine. How many for?
A Just for two.
C Smoking or non-smoking?
A Non-smoking, please.
C OK. What name?
A Taylor.

■ **You are A, the customer. Complete the conversation.**

D Good evening, sir, madam. Have you got a reservation?
A Yes, we have. For eight o'clock.
D What name?
A Taylor.
D Ah, yes. A table for two?
A That's right.
D Please follow me …

■ **This time, you are D. Complete the conversation.**

12 Restaurant

B May I have the menu?
A Of course. Here you are.

A Are you ready to order?
B Not yet. I'm waiting for someone.
A OK.

■ **You are B, the customer. Complete the conversations.**

C Sorry I'm late.
B That's OK.
C Are we having a starter?
B Yes. What would you like?
C Caesar salad.
B What about the main course?
C I'll have the salmon.
   What about you?
B I'll have the chicken. Would you like some wine?
C I'll just have mineral water.
B Sparkling or still?
C Sparkling, please.

■ **You are B. Complete the conversation.**

13 Paying

A How are you paying?
B Do you take traveller's cheques?
A No, I'm afraid not.
B Can I pay by credit card?
A Of course.

■ **You are B, the customer. Complete the conversation.**

A Please sign here.
B There you are.
A Thank you. The receipt's in the bag.
B Thanks.

■ **You are A, the shop assistant. Complete the conversation.**

A I'd like these socks, please.
B They're seven pounds fifty.
A Can you change a fifty-pound note?
B Have you got anything else?
A No, I haven't. Sorry.
B That's OK.

■ **You are A, the customer. Complete the conversation.**

A Let me pay half the bill.
B No, it's on me.
A Are you sure?
B Yes, that's fine.
A OK, thank you. I'll pay next time.

■ **You are A. Complete the conversation.**

14 Time

What's the time?
Ten thirty-five.
Are we late?
No, we've got another ten minutes. The meeting's at a quarter to eleven.

■ You are the person asking questions. Complete the conversation.

Do you know the time?
Yes, it's twenty past nine.
You're twenty minutes late.
Yes, I know. I'm very sorry. It isn't my fault. The bus was late.

■ You are the young man. Complete the conversation.

When will my car be ready?
Any time after four o'clock.
I'll be back around five.
That's fine. It'll be ready then.
OK. See you later.

■ You are the customer. Complete the conversation.

Excuse me, what time does the Chicago flight leave?
There are two. Which one?
BA 299.
It leaves at seven twenty.
Thank you.

■ You are asking about a flight. Complete the conversation.

15 Telephoning

A Can I speak to Becky, please?
B I'm sorry. I think you've got the wrong number.
A Is that 01202 097638?
B No, this is 097683.
A Oh, dear. Sorry to disturb you.
B No problem.

A Hello, can I speak to Michael Davis, please?
B Who's calling?
A This is Lisa Parsons. From Central Bank.
B Please hold. I'll put you through.

A Hello. Is Claire there?
B Yes, she is. Who is it?
A Anna. From college.
B Just a moment, Anna. I'll go and get her.
A Thanks.
B Claire! It's for you!

■ **You are B. Complete the conversations.**

16 Telephone messages

A Hello. Martin?
B No, this is Susan.
A Is Martin there?
B No, sorry. He's out. Can I take a message?
A Yes. Tell him Gloria called.
B OK. Has he got your number?
A Yes, he has.

■ **You are B. Complete the conversation.**

C Were there any messages for me?
D Yes, there was one. Gloria called.
C What did she want?
D She didn't say.
C Did you take her number?
D No, I didn't.
C Why not?
D She said you had it.

■ **You are C. Complete the conversation.**

17 Getting around

A I'm going to look at the map again.
B Are we lost?
A No.
B How far is it to the beach?
A I don't know.
B Well, are we near?
A It's somewhere near this village.
B Do you know where we are now?
A Not really, no.
B Can I look at the map?
A OK.
B The map's upside-down! We're going the wrong way!
A Oh, yes. Sorry.
B I'm going to ask someone for directions.

B Excuse me, is this the way to the beach?
C No. Turn round and go back to the main road, then turn left.
B Go back to the main road, and turn left.
C That's it.
B Thanks.

■ **You are B. Complete the conversations.**

18 Appointments

A I'd like to make an appointment, please.
B Who with?
A Dr Finley.
B And what's your name?
A Claire Barker.
B Is Friday the fifteenth OK?
A Not really. Can I see her today?
B I'm afraid she's busy today.
A How about tomorrow?
B She's free at three thirty.
A Yes, that's OK.
B Right. Wednesday the thirteenth at three thirty.

■ **You are A, the patient. Complete the conversation.**

A Can I make an appointment with Dr Kildare?
B Yes. When would you like an appointment?
A As soon as possible.
B I'm afraid he's busy this morning.
A Oh, dear. It's urgent.
B Can you come this afternoon?
A Yes, OK. What time?
B Is four o'clock OK?
A That's fine. Thank you.
B What's your name?
A Janet Green.

■ **You are B, the receptionist. Complete the conversation.**

19 Airport check-in

Checking-in
A Can I check in here?
B Can I see your ticket?
A Yes. Flight BA367 to London.
B Have you got any bags?
A Yes, just one.
B Would you like a window seat?
A Yes, I would.
B Did you pack your bag yourself?
A Sorry?
B Did you put all the things in your bag?
A Yes, I did.
B Was your bag with you at all times?
A Yes, it was.
B OK. Gate seventeen at four o'clock.
A Thank you.

At the gate
A Is this the flight to London?
B That's right. The plane's late.
A When is it going to leave?
B We're going to board the plane in thirty minutes. Please take a seat.

■ **You are A, the traveller. Complete the conversations.**

20 Tourism

A Have you been to the Tower of London yet?
B No, not yet. Have you?
A Yes, I went there yesterday.
B What was it like?
A Very interesting.

A A film, please.
B What kind? Thirty-five millimetre or APS?
A APS, please.
B Twenty-five or forty exposure?
A Forty.
B Do you want Kodak or Fuji?
A It doesn't matter. Which is cheaper?

A Excuse me, can you take a photo of us?
B OK. What do I do?
A Just press that button at the top.
B Right. Look at the camera. Smile!

■ **You are B. Complete the conversations.**

21 On a plane

A Can I see your boarding pass?
B Yes. Seat 6F.
A That's on the left. It's an aisle seat.
B Thank you.

B Excuse me.
A Yes?
B I haven't got a headset.
A Is it in the seat pocket?
B No, it isn't. I've looked.
A I'll get you one.

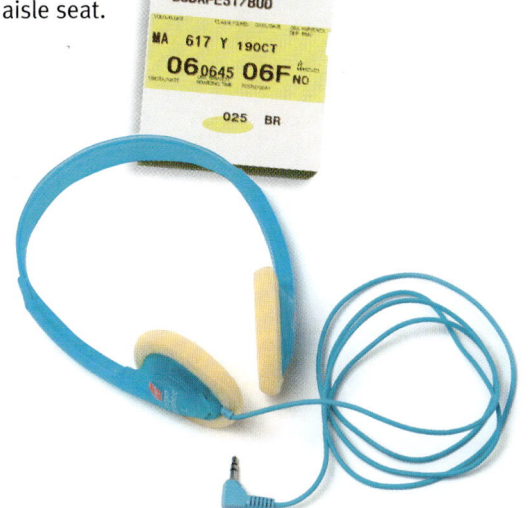

A Would you like any duty-free goods today?
B Yes, please. A bottle of whisky.
A What make?
B It doesn't matter ... that one.
 Can I pay in dollars?
A Yes, of course. That's eighteen dollars.

A Do you need a landing card?
B I don't know.
A Have you got a European Union passport?
B No, I haven't.
A Then you need one. Here you are.
B Thanks. Have you got a pen?
A I'll get you one.

■ **You are B, the traveller. Complete the conversations.**

22 At the bank

A   Is there an ATM machine here?
B   Sorry, I don't understand.
A   An Automatic Teller Machine.
B   Oh! You mean a cash machine! Yes, there's one over there.

Note: In North America, they say ATM. In the UK and Ireland, it's cash machine or cashpoint.

A   Can I change some traveller's cheques?
B   What kind are they?
A   American Express. In dollars. I want to change them for euros.
B   That's fine. How much do you want to change?
A   Five hundred dollars. What's the exchange rate?
B   It's on the board.
A   Yes, that's OK.
B   Could you sign them and date them?
A   OK. Who are they payable to?
B   The Bank of Ireland. But you can just put 'cash'.
A   Thanks.
B   How would you like the euros?
A   In twenties, please.

■ **You are A. Complete the conversations.**

Test yourself in English

How to use this section

**Inside your *3 in 1 Practice Pack* there is a square of red plastic.
When you cover the text with this square you can read the words in black,
but you can't see the words in pink.**

■
PINK
BLACK

■
PI
BLACK

Method

1 Cover the test with the red plastic square. You can see the words in black. You can't see the words in pink.
2 Remember the words in pink. Say them to yourself.
3 Do the tests after Units 5, 10, 15, 20, 25, and 30 of the Student's Book. Do the tests again a week later.

Test 1 (Units 1–5)

1. Good to *meet* you.
2. Where *are* you from?
3. What's *your* phone number?
4. 'Bye!' 'Goodbye. *See* you next week.'
5. 'How are you?' '*I'm* very well, thank you.'
6. 'How old *are* they?' 'He's eight, and she's five.'
7. 'How old are you?' '*Sorry.* That's a personal question.'
8. 'How *much* is that?' 'Nine fifty.'
9. *An* egg and bacon sandwich, please.
10. The church is about four hundred *years* old.
11. *Those* are our seats over there.
12. A pot of coffee *for* two, please.
13. '*Anything* to eat?' 'No, thanks. I'm not hungry.'
14. Have you *got* any sisters?
15. I *haven't* got any money for the car-park machine.
16. She *hasn't* got any appointments free today.
17. I've got an appointment at four *o'clock*.
18. *Has* he got a car?
19. I *don't* know. Ask him.
20. 'How *about* Wednesday?' 'Yes, that's OK. What time?'

Test 2 (Units 6–10)

1. He works in a bank.
2. Where do you work?
3. She doesn't work on Sundays.
4. Do you work in the evenings?
5. Does he work at weekends?
6. How many cinemas are there in your home town?
7. Her flight arrives at twenty-three forty-five.
8. Which platform does the London train leave from?
9. I need some information about trains, please.
10. She goes to work by car.
11. Don't talk! Be quiet.
12. Be careful! Don't move! There's a spider on the chair.
13. We're on holiday. Can you take a photo of us?
14. There's Mr and Mrs Harvey. Do you know them?
15. I can't sit outside today. It's too hot.
16. Can you count from 1 to 100 in English?
17. 'Where is it?' 'It's on the right.'
18. There aren't any shops in the village.
19. How do you travel to work?
20. Come in! Take your coat off.

Test 3 (Units 11–15)

1. There are some strawberries in the bowl.
2. There's some milk in the fridge.
3. I'm going to the supermarket. We haven't got any eggs.
4. 'Some of these, please.' 'The beans?' 'Yes.'
5. 'Whose book is that?' 'It's Tom's.'
6. I'd like a double espresso, please.
7. Would you like ice in your drink?
8. Would you like these biscuits, or those biscuits?
9. 'I'm looking for the railway station.' 'It's just around the corner.'
10. 'I'm trying to find the furniture department.' 'It's on the fifth floor.'
11. She isn't here. She's playing tennis.
12. What are you doing at the moment?
13. I really like your jacket. Is it new?
14. Do you like watching TV?
15. Thank you. I'd like a cup of tea, please.
16. I don't like tea, but I love coffee.
17. Would you like some milk in your tea?
18. 'Do you like dancing?' 'Yes, I go to a club every Friday.'
19. 'May I help you?' 'No, thanks. I'm just looking.'
20. Five at four euros. That's twenty euros altogether.

Test 4 (Units 16–20)

1 'Is it going to rain tomorrow?' 'I don't know.'
2 May is the fifth month of the year.
3 'Are you going to Jane's wedding?' 'Yes, I am.'
4 It's Friday today. It's Saturday tomorrow.
5 'Where were you yesterday?' 'I was at work.'
6 Victoria was the Queen of England from 1837 to 1901.
7 Chantel was born on 3 February 1982.
8 Were you born at home or in hospital?
9 'What do you usually have for lunch?' 'A sandwich.'
10 'Did you have a sandwich yesterday?' 'Yes, I did.'
11 We went to Paris for our honeymoon.
12 Really? Did you go by air or by sea?
13 'What did you do last night?' 'I stayed at home.'
14 'What happened in 2002?' 'I started university.'
15 When did they get married?
16 'Did you see them yesterday?' 'No, I didn't.'
17 Do you see them every day?
18 She was twenty-two last birthday.
19 We both got food poisoning on our holiday.
20 I bought a three-hour videotape.

Test 5 (Units 21–25)

1. He hardly ever eats fried food.
2. She eats in a restaurant three or four times a week.
3. How often do you see your cousins?
4. They always get up early. They do it seven days a week.
5. In England it's usually warm in July.
6. What do you usually wear to work?
7. 'What are you wearing today?' 'Jeans and a white top.'
8. Have you ever been to England?
9. She's been to France, but she hasn't been to Italy.
10. Have you ever seen a film in English?
11. I haven't been to London yet, but I'm going there next year.
12. Sorry. He isn't here. He's gone out for lunch.
13. 'Can you phone Anna?' 'Not now. I'll phone her later.'
14. Will you turn the radio off, please? I'm trying to make a phone call.
15. 'Will you do the washing-up?' 'No, I won't!'
16. 'Is that the phone?' 'Yes. It's OK. I'll answer it.'
17. I promise. It won't happen again.
18. Excuse me. Could I have a glass of water, please?
19. Will you help me with this?
20. 'Can you lend me some money?' 'How much do you want?'

Test 6 (Units 26–30)

1. 'How long will the journey take?' 'It depends on the traffic.'
2. I'm sorry, I won't be at work tomorrow. I've got 'flu.
3. 'The bus hasn't come yet. How long will it be?' 'It'll be here soon.'
4. I think it'll rain tomorrow.
5. The planet Mars is smaller than the Earth.
6. He's the best singer I've ever seen.
7. She's the most famous writer in my country.
8. Please close the door quietly. The children are sleeping.
9. She works on a computer for most of the day.
10. Paul's tall. His brother's tall too.
11. You've finished your tea. Would you like another cup?
12. What kind of films do you like watching?
13. She's two years older than me.
14. I can't come to the party. I've got to work on Saturday.
15. I couldn't go out yesterday. I was too busy.
16. When I was at school, I had to wear school uniform.
17. I want to be healthier, so I'm going to join a gym.
18. She went to the bank to get some money.
19. I was tired, so I went to bed early.
20. I went to bed early because I was tired.

Reading for pleasure

in English

WonderWorld

1 It's a big world

'Step this way. Climb into the car. Put on the safety harness. Next, please. Step this way. Climb into the next car, please. Put on the safety harness …'

WonderWorld, Florida on a Monday morning in December. There are 56,000 tourists in the theme park. It's Kelly's first day at WonderWorld and she's hot, tired, and thirsty.

'Put on the safety harness, please. Next …'

Kelly's smiling at everybody. Kelly is working on 'It's a big world.' It's a children's ride. There's a Mexican town, then a Chinese town, a Japanese train, a Brazilian football stadium, and a French restaurant. Kelly can hear the music.

'We live in a big world, you and me!

We're all happy in our big world, big world

We're as happy as we can be.'

'I can't listen to this awful music all day,' she thinks. Kelly's wearing a yellow skirt, yellow shoes, and a red coat with a yellow hat. It's Kelly's vacation job. Kelly's a student and she's working here at WonderWorld for her vacation. She helps people into the cars for the ride. She's working with Paul. Paul's wearing yellow trousers and a red coat too.

'Step this way …'

2 Happy people

A man and a woman are walking up the steps to the ride. A small girl is with them. She's wearing blue jeans, pink trainers, and a pink T-shirt. The man and woman aren't smiling.

Girl Hey! Mommy! I don't like this ride!
Mother But honey, this is 'It's a big world'. All the kids love this ride.
Girl Well, I don't! This is a ride for little kids! I want to go on 'Fly Into Space'.
Mother Not now, honey …
Girl But this ride is …

The little girl is saying some very bad words. And everybody is listening. Her mother's face is very red.

Mother Don't say that! Not here! This is WonderWorld, honey. Everybody's happy …

Girl Not me! I want to go on 'Fly Into Space'. I want to …
Father Don't say, 'I want …', honey. Say 'I'd like …'
Girl I'd like to go on 'Fly Into Space'! I'd like to go on 'Fly Into Space'! I'd like …

Paul is smiling at the little girl.

Paul Hi, honey. Climb into this car, you're going to enjoy this ride …
Girl Go away, dog face! I want to go …

The father puts the little girl into the car. Her mother and father climb into the car, too. The little girl is crying now, but the cars move on and the ride is starting. Her mother and father aren't enjoying their day. A woman is standing next to Kelly. It's Ms Garcia, Kelly's supervisor.

Ms Garcia Kelly, are you enjoying your first day?
Kelly Yes, Ms Garcia.
Ms Garcia Well, I need you on 'Fly Into Space'. I don't usually put people on 'Fly Into Space' on their first day, but someone isn't at work today. Paul's OK here. He doesn't need you now. Can you come with me?
Kelly OK. Uh, bye, Paul. See you!

3 Under WonderWorld

Ms Garcia is opening a door. Kelly follows her. They go down some steps. Tourists don't see all of WonderWorld. There are rooms and tunnels under the theme park. You can get to every ride that way. The tunnels are clean and new, like everything in the park.

Ms Garcia Do you know "Fly Into Space'?
Kelly Yes, everyone knows "Fly Into Space".

And everyone does. It's on every TV advert for WonderWorld. It's a roller-coaster ride, but it's a roller-coaster ride in the dark. You can't see anything, and it's very fast. The small spaceships have seats for two people, and the safety harnesses are strong. The ride turns 360° four times. When people arrive at WonderWorld, a lot of them go to 'Fly Into Space' first. When the park opens at eight o'clock, people run to 'Fly Into Space'. Now, at ten thirty in the morning, the lines for 'Fly Into Space' are very long.

The tunnel is about five hundred metres long between 'It's a big world' and 'Fly Into Space'. Ms Garcia is talking about the ride.

Ms Garcia It's very safe. People can't open the safety harnesses, and the spaceships can't come off the tracks. The ride can't move when a safety harness is open. We can stop the ride at any time.
Kelly And what do I do?
Ms Garcia You check the safety harnesses. Every time someone gets into a car, you pull the safety harness down, and you check it.

Then the tunnel is going up. At the end, Ms Garcia opens a door. There's a room with a lot of silver suits and silver shoes.

Ms Garcia What size are you?
Kelly Size eight.
Ms Garcia You can find your size over there. Put the yellow skirt and shoes on the table.

4 'Fly Into Space'

'Fly Into Space' is in a big building. Kelly can hear the spaceships on the roller-coaster, and loud music is playing too. There is a long line of people. At the end of the line, there are two tracks with spaceships on them. A man in a silver suit asks people to go left or right to the spaceships. A man and a woman in silver suits are helping people into the spaceships and checking the harnesses. Ms Garcia is standing by the left track.

Ms Garcia Kelly! Over here! This is Jessica. Watch her. Watch her for five minutes. Then Jessica, you can go for your coffee, and Kelly can check the harnesses.

Jessica checks every harness carefully. There's a red light when the harness is open, and a green light when it is closed. But Jessica checks every time. Then the spaceships move away and climb slowly up the roller coaster.

Jessica Are you OK now? Can you do it?
Kelly Yes. I'm fine.
Jessica I'm going for my coffee. Twenty minutes, OK? You can ask Michael anything.
Kelly Michael?
Jessica That's Michael over there on the right track.

Twenty minutes, then Jessica comes back with Ms Garcia.

Ms Garcia Kelly, come with me. You're going to check sizes.
Kelly Check sizes? I don't understand.
Ms Garcia Small kids can't go on the ride. They're too small for the harnesses.
Kelly Small kids? How old?
Ms Garcia The question is 'what size?' not 'how old?'. We can't ask everybody, 'How old is your kid?'. We've got a sign. It's over here.

They walk by the line of people. It's very long. Then Kelly can see light. They're by the door to the building. There's a sign, with a red line across it.

BE SAFE!

Are you as tall as this line? If not, you can't ride "Fly Into Space".
NO FOOD • NO DRINK • NO SMOKING

A man in a silver suit is checking people.

Daniel OK, young man. Stand here. That's all right. Step this way, enjoy the ride! And you, young lady. OK, you're tall! Enjoy the ride! Walk that way. Excuse me, stand here. Oh, no, honey. I'm very sorry. Next year for you. Oh, excuse me, sir. No food or drink on the ride, or in the line. You can finish your ice-cream here, then you can go into the ride.

Ms Garcia Kelly, meet Daniel. He checks the sizes.

Daniel Hey, Kelly.

Kelly Hey.

Ms Garcia You can go for a coffee break, Daniel. Kelly's going to check the sizes for an hour.

Daniel OK. Be careful, Kelly. These kids try anything! Look at their shoes, not at their faces. They stand on their toes!

5 How tall are you?

Kelly checks the sizes for about forty-five minutes. A few people get angry when their kids can't ride, but people usually understand. Then Kelly sees the man and woman from 'It's a Big World'. They aren't smiling. The small girl is with them. Now she's got a WonderWorld baseball cap. She's eating an ice-cream.

Mother All right, honey, we're here. This is 'Fly Into Space'.

Father There's a long line, honey. We can go and get a hot dog, and we can come back this afternoon.

Girl I want to go now. NOW! I WANT TO GO NOW!

Kelly looks at the line on the sign, and at the little girl. This is going to be difficult.

Kelly Excuse me, honey, how tall are you? Can you …

But the little girl is walking past her. Kelly holds the little girl's arm.

Kelly Wait, honey. Can you stand by the sign …

Girl Aah! Mommy! Mommy! She's hurting my arm!

People are looking at Kelly now.

Mother Don't hold her arm! Who are you?

Kelly I'm sorry, ma'am. I need to check her size.

Mother I'm her mother. She's OK. Come on, honey.

Kelly No, ma'am. You don't understand. I need to check. She isn't very tall, and it isn't safe.

Father Look, she's all right. She wants to go on the ride.

Girl Daddy! Can I go on the ride NOW?

Kelly I'm very sorry, sir. This is my job. Can she stand over here?

The little girl stands by the sign with her ice-cream. Kelly looks down at her shoes. The shoes are thick trainers, and the little girl is standing on her toes.

Kelly Stand down, honey. Don't stand on your toes.

The little girl isn't two or three centimetres too small. She's six or seven centimetres too small.

Kelly Sorry, honey. Next year for you.

Now the little girl is crying. The man and woman are angry.

Man This park is twenty-five dollars for a little kid, and then she can't go on the ride!

Kelly I'm sorry, sir. But this ride isn't safe for small kids.

Father Twenty-five dollars! Then four dollars for a hot dog, three dollars for a cola, fifteen dollars for a hat and two seventy-five for that ice-cream …

Mother Can we talk to your supervisor?

Kelly Yes, you can go to the park information office. Ask for Ms Garcia.

Then the little girl runs! She's running very fast into the building. She's running past the line of people.

Mother Hey, you! Stop her!

Kelly Excuse me?

Mother Stop her! That ride isn't safe for small kids!

6 Up into space

Kelly is running past the long line of people. Where is the little girl? She can't see her. Then it's the end of the line. Kelly can see Jessica on the left track and Michael on the right track. They're helping people into the spaceships and checking their safety harnesses. There are a lot of people. They're waiting for the ride.

Michael is checking a safety harness. The green light goes on. Michael stands away, and the spaceship is moving slowly along the track and climbing up the roller-coaster. Then Kelly sees pink and blue – the little girl is running between some people. She throws her ice-cream down, then she runs past Michael and then she's on the spaceship. She's holding the back of the spaceship, and it's moving up the track. The woman in the back seat of the spaceship is looking round in surprise.

Kelly Hold her arm! Quick! Hold her arm.

But the woman can't turn in the safety harness. Michael runs to a small control. There's a big red button on the control, with the word STOP on it. But Michael stands on the little girl's ice-cream, falls and crashes into the control. He hurts his head, and he doesn't push the button.

Michael Quick! When the spaceship gets to the top of the roller coaster it's going to come down at sixty miles an hour!

Kelly can see the spaceship. It's climbing slowly into the dark. She runs to the button and pushes hard. Then all of the lights in the building are on! The spaceships that are climbing up the roller-coaster stop. But the spaceships that are coming down the roller-coaster don't stop. The music isn't playing now. People are shouting from the spaceships.

Jessica talks into a microphone.

Jessica Please don't move. Everything is safe. The ride is going to start again in a few minutes. Please don't move. Everything is safe.

Michael gets up. He's holding his head.

Kelly Are you OK, Michael?
Michael I don't know, it's my head … it's hurting.
Kelly Sit down.

Kelly can hear crying. It's the little girl. The spaceship is on the track, but the track is going up at an angle of 45°. The little girl is holding the back of the spaceship. The woman in the back of the spaceship is shouting.

Woman She can't hold it … and I can't move! Do something!

Kelly looks up at the track. Then she starts to climb up the track. There's black oil from the track on her silver suit. She shouts to the little girl.

Kelly It's OK, honey. Hold on! I'm coming! You're going to be OK.

Kelly is twenty metres up the track now, and the sides of the tunnel stop. Then there are no sides. Kelly looks down. It's a long way. She can see the roller-coaster tracks going down and turning.

Forty metres. The angle is 45°. Ten more metres. Kelly holds the spaceship and puts her arm around the little girl.

Kelly OK, honey. I've got you now. You're safe.

The little girl is crying. The woman in the back of the spaceship is crying, too.

Kelly What's your name, honey?
Girl Sally. I want to go on the ride.
Kelly OK, Sally, you're on the ride now, honey.

Michael is shouting up at her.

Michael Is everything OK, Kelly?
Kelly Yes. I've got her.
Michael We're coming to get you.

One minute later, Jessica and Michael are with her. They're standing next to the spaceship. But how? Kelly looks down. There are steps next to the track.

Michael We can't all climb up the track, you know. We just walk up the emergency steps, Kelly.

They all walk down the steps. Jessica goes to the microphone.

Jessica The ride is going to start in ten seconds. Everything is all right.

Then it's dark again, and the spaceships are climbing slowly up the roller-coaster. Kelly looks down. The little girl is holding Kelly's hand. The girl's mother and father arrive. The girl's mother runs over to her.

Mother Are you OK, honey? Hey! What's this on her new T-shirt! It's oil! Harry, look, there's oil on her new T-shirt!

Father Oil! Fourteen dollars and fifty-nine cents for a new T-shirt, and there's oil on it! I'm not coming to this park again.

Ms Garcia is standing behind them.

Ms Garcia Please don't, sir. Please don't come again.
Father Who are you?
Ms Garcia My name's Garcia, sir. I'm the supervisor. Is the kid OK, Kelly? And you?
Kelly I'm fine. And Sally's fine, too.

The little girl is smiling.

Ms Garcia I'm sorry about the oil, honey. But I'm going to give you a nice new WonderWorld T-shirt.
Girl Really!
Ms Garcia Really. And you can't go on this ride, but I'm going to show you something. You're going to see under WonderWorld! Kelly, you can take Sally to the tunnels under the ride. Show her everything, OK?

Mastergame

1 Robberies

Don Wolfe walked into the coffee bar, and took a seat at the counter. He was the only customer and the man behind the counter came over immediately.

'Good afternoon,' he said. 'What would you like?'

'Just a coffee, please,' said Don. 'Are you Mr Powell?'

'Yes, that's me,' the man replied.

'I'm Don Wolfe from the Castershire Evening News. I telephoned this morning.'

'Yes, that's right,' said the man, and he put a cup of coffee in front of Don. 'What can I do for you?'

'I'm writing an article about the robberies in the town centre. You've been robbed four times, haven't you?'

'Yes. Four times in two weeks,' the man replied, 'and I'm not the only one. Most of the shops in this area have had robberies. It's funny, I've been here for ten years, and there were never any problems until two weeks ago.'

'The thieves are always young teenagers. Is that correct?'

'Yes, thirteen, fourteen years old. One buys a coffee and while I'm getting it, another one opens the cash register.'

'How much do they take?' asked Don.

'That's another thing. They usually only take a few coins. That's all. Why don't you ask some of the other shops around here?'

'I'm going to,' said Don, and he stood up. 'How much is the coffee?'

'One fifty, but you needn't pay. It's OK.'

'Thank you very much,' said Don. 'But I need some coins for the car park. Can you change a note for me?'

'You're lucky. I've just been to the bank. I don't usually have any coins. That's another funny thing. Every customer wants change. Every kid asks for coins. I think it's the new video games arcade. It's just along the street. Everybody wants money for the machines.'

Don thought for a moment, 'That's interesting,' he said. 'Which way is it to the arcade?'

'Just turn left outside the door. It's about four doors from here. You can't miss it. You'll hear the noise.'

2 Video games

Don walked along the street. There it was. A huge neon sign, 'Video games. All the latest machines.' Don stopped outside. He could hear the games. Rat-tat-tat-tat! Kapow! Zoom! Crash! He walked into the dark arcade. There was a long queue of kids at the back of the arcade. Three machines were making all the noise. There were fifty or sixty machines in the arcade, but the kids were using only three. They were queuing to play on them. Don looked at the other machines. Nobody was playing on any of them. He walked over to the queue. None of the kids were talking. They were all looking at the three games at the front. They were all the same. They were all called *Mastergame*. Don moved towards the front of the queue.

    A girl held his arm, 'Hey, there's a queue. Can't you see?'

    'Er ... I don't want to play. I'm just looking.'

    'Well, wait for your turn! We all want to watch.'

    Don joined the queue. A large sign said, 'One game only, then go to the back of the queue.' The games were very short – sometimes thirty seconds, sometimes a minute. The longest game he saw was two minutes, and then everyone clapped when the player finished. At last, Don was near the front. The player controlled a spaceship and fired missiles at alien spaceships. It looked the same as any other 3D video game. Why was it so popular? Don was at the front now. He sat down and put in two coins and started to move his spaceship forward.

    The alien spaceships were beautiful. A green and gold light shimmered around them. He couldn't look away from the screen. Twenty seconds later his spaceship was destroyed. He wanted to try again. He put his hand in his pocket for more money. Suddenly everybody was shouting.

    'Hey! Only one game!'

    'Go to the back of the queue!'

    'You've had your turn!'

    He turned away from the machine and started to walk out. Then he stopped. This was the back of the queue ... just one more game. He had to try again. No, it was silly ... but just one more game ... one more, that's all.

    'I need more money. I've got to have more money. Next time I can win. I know it.' A boy was speaking. He was about fifteen.

    Don spoke to him, 'Do you often play *Mastergame*?'

    'Often! I've played twelve times today. You have to queue for a long time, but next week they're getting five more machines. Isn't that wonderful?'

    Don felt happy. Five more machines! Shorter queues! He could play every day. It was wonderful. He joined the queue and he put his hand into his pocket for more change. He didn't have any! He looked round.

There was a sign saying 'Change given here'. He left the queue and went to the cash desk. Suddenly he stopped. That was it! The kids had to play. That was the reason for the robberies and for the requests for change. *Mastergame* was like a drug. It was an addiction.

3 A new game

A large man with grey hair was sitting at the cash desk. Don said, 'That *Mastergame* is really good. Are you getting more machines?'

The man looked up. 'Yeah. Five more machines next week.'

Don smiled and said, 'Are they very expensive?'

'Oh, you can't buy them. They aren't for sale. Mastervideo owns them.'

'Mastervideo?' asked Don.

'Yeah. They put in the machines and they take 90% of the money. I get 10%. I get 50% on all the other machines but 10% of *Mastergame* is better than 50% of the others.'

'Really?' said Don

'Yeah. We have to empty the machines twenty times a day. They're fantastic.'

'I've never seen them before,' said Don.

'No. We're the first arcade with *Mastergame*. You see, Mastervideo is a local company. Their factory is just outside town. They're testing *Mastergame* here.'

'You're very lucky,' said Don.

'Yeah,' said the man, 'and I can play it for nothing when we're closed. I don't have to pay.'

'Do you play it?' asked Don.

'Oh, yeah. I love it,' said the man. 'I played it for seven hours last night. I couldn't stop. It's the best game I've ever played.'

Don got back to the office and sat down at his desk. There was a story for the newspaper here. A good story. He picked up the telephone directory. There it was, 'Mastervideo, Avenue 4, New Trading Estate, Casterford. Tel. 01229 361852'. Don keyed in the number carefully. A woman answered.

'Hello, Mastervideo?'

'Hello. This is the Castershire Evening News. I wanted to ask you about *Mastergame*.'

'Wait.'

Don waited for a few minutes. Then he heard a man's voice.

'What do you want?'

'It's about *Mastergame* …'

'Yes?'

'It's very popular.'

'Yes.'

'Can I come and interview you about it?'

'No. No, you see it's very new. We don't want other companies to know about it. Goodbye.'

4 At the factory

Don drove slowly past the factory later that day. There were no windows. There was a high electric fence and two guards with dogs at the gate. He drove past the factory twice, then he went to a friend's house. Julie was a scientist. She was an expert on computers. Don told her about *Mastergame*.

'New games are always more popular,' she said.

'This is different, Julie. Come and see.'

They drove to the town centre. Don parked carefully outside the video arcade. A sign on the door said, 'Closed', but a light was on. Don pushed the door. It was open. They walked in quietly. They could hear a loud humming noise. *Mastergame* was on. Nobody was playing. The large man was sitting in front of one machine. He was asleep.

'Look at him,' said Don. 'He's tired because he plays *Mastergame* all night.'

'Show me the game,' said Julie.

Don felt happy. He put two coins into the next machine and the alien spaceship appeared. He smiled. He felt wonderful. He began to move his spaceship. Suddenly the screen went black. He looked round angrily.

'I did it. I stopped the machine,' said Julie. 'Get me a screwdriver.'

An hour later Julie looked up.

'This is it,' she said. 'It's completely new. It hypnotises you, then it sends messages for a very short time, for a two-hundreth of a second. It tells you that you must play again.'

'But, that's terrible!' said Don. 'The kids are stealing money to play.'

Julie smiled. 'You're the journalist,' she said. 'You can stop it. Just tell everyone about it.'

5 One more cup of coffee

The *Mastergame* article was a great success. It was in the Castershire Evening News, then in the national daily newspapers. There was a television programme about it. When the TV cameras went to Mastervideo's factory, it was empty.

Don Wolfe got a better job. He became a journalist for the Daily News, a national newspaper. He had to move to London. On his last day in Casterford he returned to the coffee bar where it all started, weeks before. It wasn't empty now. It was full of people. People were queuing outside. Don went in. The counter wasn't there. Now there was a long row of automatic vending machines, a coffee machine, a sandwich machine, a cake machine and a donut machine. Kids were putting money into the vending machines. Don saw Mr Powell. He was sitting at a table with a plastic coffee cup. Mr Powell waved.

'Do you like the new restaurant?' he asked.

'Yes, it's very nice,' said Don.

'Get a cup of coffee and sit down,' said Mr Powell.

Don went to the nearest machine and put in some money. It was expensive for a coffee machine. Lights began flashing as the machine operated. They were lovely lights. They were green and gold and shimmering. There was a wonderful smell of coffee, too. He wanted a coffee very much. He loved coffee. He picked up the coffee cup. A sandwich! He was really hungry. He wanted a sandwich. A tuna sandwich. He put in his coins. Lights flashed again. He could here Mr Powell's voice. It sounded a long way away.

'It's wonderful coffee. I drink nearly twenty cups a day.'

The sandwich arrived. It was in a green and gold plastic box. Don looked at the box. It said *Mastersandwich*. Don smiled. He was very hungry. A donut! He was going to buy a donut.

OXFORD
UNIVERSITY PRESS

Great Clarendon Street, Oxford OX2 6DP

Oxford University Press is a department of the University of Oxford. It furthers the University's objective of excellence in research, scholarship, and education by publishing worldwide in

Oxford New York

Auckland Cape Town Dar es Salaam
Hong Kong Karachi Kuala Lumpur Madrid
Melbourne Mexico City Nairobi New Delhi
Shanghai Taipei Toronto

With offices in

Argentina Austria Brazil Chile Czech Republic
France Greece Guatemala Hungary Italy Japan
Poland Portugal Singapore South Korea
Switzerland Thailand Turkey Ukraine Vietnam

OXFORD and OXFORD ENGLISH are registered trade marks of Oxford University Press in the UK and in certain other countries

© Oxford University Press / Three Vee Limited 2004

The moral rights of the author have been asserted

Database right Oxford University Press (maker)

First published 2004

2014 2013 2012 2011
10 9 8 7

No unauthorized photocopying

All rights reserved. No part of this publication may be reproduced, stored in a retrieval system, or transmitted, in any form or by any means, without the prior permission in writing of Oxford University Press, or as expressly permitted by law, or under terms agreed with the appropriate reprographics rights organization. Enquiries concerning reproduction outside the scope of the above should be sent to the ELT Rights Department, Oxford University Press, at the address above

You must not circulate this book in any other binding or cover and you must impose this same condition on any acquirer

Any websites referred to in this publication are in the public domain and their addresses are provided by Oxford University Press for information only. Oxford University Press disclaims any responsibility for the content

ISBN-13: 978 0 19 434057 1

Typeset in Meta

Printed in China

ACKNOWLEDGEMENTS

Designed by Richard Morris, Stonesfield Design

Authors' Acknowledgements:
In a complex series like this, which has taken several years to prepare, pilot and produce, many people are involved and have creative input. We wish to thank the many people at OUP who participated in making this book.

We would like to add our further personal thanks to, Catherine Smith and Karen Jamieson (Project Managers and Student's Book editors), Sally Cooke (Editor, 3 in 1 Practice pack, Teacher's Book and Photocopiables), and Richard Morris (Designer for all components).

Illustrations by:
Mark Duffin: pp.7, 40

Commissioned photography by:
Adrian Arbib: pp.24 (2, 3, 4), 25 (6), 42 (7), 53 (bl), 54 (bl, br), 55 (all except bl), 56 (br), 62, 63 (top)
Steve Betts: pp.23 (8) 53 (tr, br), 55 (bl)
Gareth Boden: p.56 (tr)
Richard Morris:pp.23(1/2/3/4), 37, 73

We would like to thank the following for permission to reproduce photographs:
Oxford University Press/Hemera Technologies for all photographs except where credited otherwise.
BAA Aviation Photo Library p71 (In-Press Photography/Anthony Charlton); BMW p41 (top); Corbis UK Ltd. pp.34 (15) (Clive Druett/Papilio), 38 (14/15) (Ray Juno), 38 (18) (Sergio Pitamitz), 54 (tr) (Ronnen Eshel), 74 (Ariel Skelley); Ford Motor Company (UK) p41 (bottom); NASA pp.40 (9) (Susan Terebey/Extrasolar Research Corp.), 40 (10) (Hubble Heritage Team (AURA/STScI), 40 (11); Oxford University Press pp.23 (5), 26 (2/3, 13, 15, 16), 40 (6, 7, 8), 58, 65, 72 (top); Siemens AG p43 (14, 15); Peter Viney: pp.26 (1, 4–12, 14), 35 (all), 36 (all), 59, Zooid Pictures p28 (5)